To Your Health

To Your Health

Gospel Perspectives on Nurturing the Mind, Body, and Spirit

Brent Q. Hafen, Ph.D.
Keith J. Karren, Ph.D.
Kathryn J. Frandsen
N. Lee Smith, M.D.

Covenant Communications, Inc.

Published by Covenant Communications, Inc.
American Fork, Utah

Printed in the United States of America
First Printing: August 1998

05 04 03 02 01 00 99 98   10 9 8 7 6 5 4 3 2 1

ISBN 1-57734-299-2

Table of Contents

Practicing believers obviously experience life's share of personal sorrow, family difficulties, illness, and pain. Yet studies are finding that religiously committed persons derive from their faith an ability to more ably cope, overcome, and find meaning—rather than hopelessness—in life's challenges. For them, the abundant life promised by the scriptures becomes a living, even measurable reality. — ELIZABETH VANDENBERGHE

INTRODUCTION

Religion and Health

Until recently, the benefits of a religious life were not widely recognized among the world's scientific community. But a growing number of studies over the past few decades have led an increasing number of physicians, psychologists, sociologists, and scientists to conclude that religion offers a better life emotionally, mentally, and physically. In fact, concluded one study, "faith and religious devotion constitute the strongest indicator for a worthwhile life."[1]

As Elder Neal A. Maxwell taught, "Jesus, the great physician, came to heal the spiritually sick—all of us."[2] That the Savior and the Church can offer spiritual healing has been commonly accepted through the ages. What is new about scientific curiosity is the unexpected finding that religion itself heals *physically.*

Religion is a science that defines a relationship with God. It is "the personal beliefs, values, and activities pertinent to that which is supernatural, mysterious, and awesome, which transcends immediate situations, and which pertains to questions of final cause and ultimate ends of man and the universe."[3] Science now tells us that people with active religious faith and strong religious affiliation generally enjoy better health:

> The "highly religious" (as many researchers call them) of many sects and creeds lead markedly different lives, empirically and statistically, than those who are less committed or those who are nonbelieving: they can literally expect not only to be happier and healthier, but also to have strong marriages, stronger families, and stronger inclinations to help others.[4]

Extensive research indicates that active participation in a church boosts health,[5] acts as a buffer against stress, and may even prolong life. Religion apparently helps protect health in a variety of ways. One is through social integration and support. We know that strong social support protects health, and for some Americans, "becoming an active member of a religious congregation can provide the tradition and social support lacking in their community."[6] People who are active in a church are not as likely to be lonely; members of a church are much like members of an extended family; they provide comfort, companionship, and even material assistance when needed.

Research also shows that people with strong religious commitment are more concerned for others, much less likely to be prejudiced, and have an easier time forgiving. According to George H. Gallup, Jr., and Timothy Jones, religious commitment boosts compassion, tolerance, and ethical behavior, qualities that in turn boost the amount of available social support. Religion itself also strengthens the sources of social support critical to health and well-being. For example, religion tends to keep marriages together; research over the last sixty years has consistently found that highly religious people tend to have more satisfying marriages[7] and stronger families, which are the basic unit of social support.

Religion also protects health by helping members establish a personal relationship with deity. People who have an interactive, caring relationship with God have higher self-worth and a greater sense of spiritual well-being; they are significantly less distressed and psychologically better adjusted.[8] The Church of Jesus Christ of Latter-day Saints goes a step further: not only can we have a personal relationship with God, it teaches, but we are in a very real sense *related to God.* Modern-day revelation to prophets in this dispensation confirms the truth that God is the literal father of our spirits and that we may become like he is. Through obedience, we are promised we can obtain all the Father has. President Spencer W. Kimball gave an insightful perspective to that doctrine when he taught:

> One of the great teachings of the Lord Jesus Christ was that you and I carry within us immense possibilities. In urging us to be perfect as our Father in Heaven is perfect, Jesus was not taunting us or teasing us. He was telling us a powerful truth about our possibilities and about our potential. It is a truth almost too stunning to contemplate.[9]

A third way religion protects health is by providing a framework of meaning by which to make sense of life. Religion offers faith and hope; it fosters a more positive attitude toward illness, pain, or disability. It provides help in adversity. Elder Russell M. Nelson advises, "It matters not that giants of tribulation torment you. Your prayerful access to help is just as real as when David battled his Goliath."[10]

The belief that life has meaning brings with it a sense of purpose. For Latter-day Saints, it provides the plan of salvation: knowledge of where we came from, a reason for what we are doing here, and the promise of exaltation beyond this life. The doctrine that perhaps has the greatest potential to shape our existence is the one that affirms our divine origin:

> As children of God we are somebody. He will build us, mold us, and magnify us if we will but hold our heads up, our arms out, and walk with him. What a great blessing to be created in his image and know of our true potential in and through him! What a great blessing to know that in his strength we can do all things![11]

Religious commitment has also been shown to enhance mental health.[12] That may be particularly true of the gospel, which brings with it the solace that soothes. "Are there times in our lives when we think we have been forsaken by God, or by our fellow men, or by our families?" asks Elder Robert D. Hales. "Those are the moments when we have to turn to Christ and endure."[13] President Harold B. Lee observed, "Just as a flood-lighted temple is more beautiful in a severe storm or a heavy fog, so the gospel of Jesus Christ is more glorious in times of inward storm and of personal sorrow and tormenting conflict."[14]

Finally, religion protects health by promoting specific patterns of personal lifestyle that contribute to good health, such as eating healthy, nutritious foods; avoiding tobacco, alcohol, and harmful drugs; and avoiding sexual promiscuity. All are tenets of our faith. The characteristic good health and long life of Latter-day Saints, as shown in numerous studies, may also be explained by a gospel that discourages hostility, anger, and negativism—that promotes love, concern for others, service, charity, hope, faith, and optimism, all of which boost health and strengthen immunity. It may be explained by a faith that focuses on the family, endorses the sanctity of marriage, embraces hope, and prescribes prayer.

As President Joseph Fielding Smith wrote, the fruits of this religion "are flavored with the sweets of heaven, and they impart health and life to the soul."[15]

Entering the Salt Lake Valley through a narrow passageway in the sheer canyon walls, President Brigham Young propped himself on his elbow and quietly affirmed, "This is the right place." Of God's plan of salvation, says Elder Neal A. Maxwell, it can be said that "This is the process!"[16] It endows us with the ability to make changes, to improve where needed. As Elder David B. Haight suggests:

> Life is a competition not with others, but with ourselves. We should seek each day to live stronger, better, truer lives; each day to master some weakness of yesterday; each day to repair a mistake; each day to surpass ourselves.[17]

Those challenges may seem insurmountable to some, but the religious discover the source of power that makes all things possible. Only Jesus Christ, said President Ezra Taft Benson, "is uniquely qualified to provide that hope, that confidence, and that strength to overcome the world and rise above our human failings."[18]

Finally, our religious perspective as Latter-day Saints gives us the capacity to apply gospel principles in our search for health and well-being. Where some might feel helpless against the factors that cause illness, we have the ability to recognize truth and a source of strength to which we can turn. When we work to implement change, as Elder Marvin J. Ashton said, we should not doubt our ability or delay our worthy impressions. "With God's help," he urged, "you cannot fail. He will give you the courage to participate in meaningful change and purposeful living."[19]

END NOTES

1. Elizabeth VanDenBerghe, "Religion and the Abundant Life," *Ensign,* October 1994, p. 33.
2. Neal A. Maxwell, *A More Excellent Way: Essays on Leadership for Latter-day Saints* (Salt Lake City: Deseret Book, 1973), p. 64.
3. Harold G. Koenig, James N. Kvale, and Carolyn Ferrel, "Religion and Well-Being in Later Life," *The Gerontologist,* Vol. 28, No. 1, 1988, pp. 18-27.
4. Elizabeth VanDenBerghe, "Religion and the Abundant Life," *Ensign,* October 1994, p. 32.
5. Leonard A. Sagan, *The Health of Nations* (New York: Basic Books, Inc., 1987), p. 137.
6. Emrika Padus, *The Complete Guide to Your Emotions and Your Health* (Emmaus, Penn.: Rodale Press, 1986), p. 462.
7. Elizabeth VanDenBerghe, "Religion and the Abundant Life," *Ensign,* October 1994, p. 39.
8. *Ibid,* p. 34.
9. Spencer W. Kimball, *Conference Report,* April 1988.
10. Russell M. Nelson, *Ensign,* May 1988, p. 21.
11. Marvin J. Ashton, *Conference Report,* April 1973.

12. Hafen, Brent Q., Keith J. Karren, Kathryn J. Frandsen, N. Lee Smith, *Mind/Body Health: The Effects of Attitudes, Emotions, and Relationships* (Needham Heights, Mass.: Allyn and Bacon, 1996), pp. 395-96.
13. Robert D. Hales, "Lessons from the Atonement That Help Us to Endure to the End," *Ensign,* November 1985, p. 20.
14. Harold B. Lee, *Conference Report,* April 1965, p. 16.
15. Joseph Fielding Smith, *Gospel Doctrine*, comp. by John A. Widtsoe (Salt Lake City: Deseret Book, 1919), p. 92.
16. Neal A. Maxwell, "Be of Good Cheer," *Ensign,* November 1982, p. 67.
17. David B. Haight, "The Responsibility of Young Aaronic Priesthood Bearers," *Ensign,* May 1981, p. 42.
18. Ezra Taft Benson, *Conference Report,* October 1983, p. 5.
19. Marvin J. Ashton, *Conference Report,* April 1983, p. 44.

The Body and the Spirit of Man Are Bound Together

The Savior's constant desire and effort were to implant in the mind right thoughts, pure motives, noble ideas, knowing full well that right words and actions would eventually follow. He taught what modern physiology and psychology confirm—that hate, jealousy, and other evil passions destroy a man's physical vigor and efficiency.

— DAVID O. MCKAY

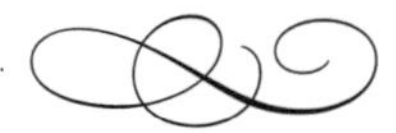

CHAPTER

I

The Mind-Body Connection

We know through divine revelation that each human being consists of both body and spirit. The scriptures are explicit regarding the separation of the physical body from the spiritual body: "And the Gods formed man from the dust of the ground, and took his spirit, and put it into him; and breathed into his nostrils the breath of life, and man became a living soul" (Abraham 5:7).

Each person's body is but the tabernacle in which his or her spirit dwells. As President David O. McKay taught, "the real man is an immortal spirit, which 'intelligence or the light of truth' animated as an individual entity before the body was begotten, and this spiritual entity with all its distinguishing traits will continue after the body ceases to respond to its earthly environment."[1]

It is the spirit, not the body, in which feelings and emotions originate. As detailed in *The Encyclopedia of Mormonism*, the spirit displays the entire range of "emotions, passions, and intellectual experiences exhibited by mortals, including love, anger, hate, envy, knowledge, obedience, rebellion, jealousy, repentance, loyalty, activity, thought, and comprehension."[2]

Part of that eternal spirit is the miracle we know as the mind. "The sentient, conscious, and intelligent part of man—the part that perceives, feels, wills, and thinks—is called the mind," wrote Elder Bruce R. McConkie. "To those who rule an Omnipotent Creator out of their views, who suppose that all things exist by mere evolutionary chance, the mind of man is an inexplicable mystery. But to those who know about God and his eternal purposes, it is clear that the mind of man rests in the eternal spirit."[3]

The notion of eternity presupposes endless existence—an infinite span that has no beginning and no end. Divine revelation teaches us that there was a life before this one, a period during which our spirits were created and we accepted the impending challenge of mortality. It teaches, too, that this life is but an instant in the perpetual span of eternity, and that after this life we will, if worthy, use the lessons we have learned here to further the creation begun by our Father.

We know that our spirits were created during the preexistence, but that our intelligence—the entity we think of as our mind—was not created, but has existed forever. We know, too, that it will continue to exist forever. The mind, Elder Bruce R. McConkie continued, was "present with the pre-existent spirit; it will be present with the disembodied spirit in the sphere immediately following mortality. Man's intelligence is in his spirit and not in the natural or mortal body."[4]

We are, then, composed of two separate entities: the spirit—which houses the mind and directs the emotions—and the body. Yet the two, though separate, are unquestionably connected. Hugh Nibley teaches that "there are ties between the body and the mind. . . . The body does play a definite role in the mind and the spirit."[5] The spirit, taught Brigham Young, is "intimately connected" with the tabernacle, or physical body. The spirit is the invisible center of thought and emotion; the body, "formed and organized for that express purpose," carries out what the spirit directs.

President John Taylor compared the spirit–body relationship to a steam engine. Despite all its power, steam, when released, rapidly evaporates into the atmosphere. Contained in a steam engine, however, it becomes a thing of tremendous force. The spirit, "quick, subtle, refined, lively, animate, energetic, and eternal," would be "comparatively useless" without the body: the tangible, material object through which it exercises its force.[6]

"The great principle of happiness consists in having a body," taught the Prophet Joseph Smith. "The devil has no body, and herein is his punishment. . . . When cast out by the Savior he asked to go into the herd of swine, showing that he would prefer a swine's body to having none."[7]

The mind is not only tied to the body, but can exert a powerful influence over it—a truth now being acknowledged by growing numbers of medical researchers. Apparently, how we feel and think has a great deal to do with the health of our physical body. "There is a tendency to think of fitness solely in terms of physical [fitness], in terms of bodily strength," wrote President Ezra Taft Benson. "But to be truly fit, truly equal to the demands of life, requires much more than bodily strength. It involves the mind and the training of the mind, the emotions and their use and control. Yes, and it involves the soul and the spiritual growth, too."[8] Spiritual strength, says President Benson, promotes positive thinking, positive ideals, positive habits, and positive attitudes, qualities, he says, that not only give purpose and perspective to life, but also promote physical well-being.[9]

One of the clearest examples of the mind's power over the body occurs in the book of Alma. Zeezrom, "a man who was expert in the devices of the devil" (Alma 11:21), had gone among the people, discounting the truths taught by Alma and Amulek. At one point, Zeezrom offered to pay Amulek, a new convert, six onties of silver—a great deal of money—if he would deny the existence of a supreme being. This may have been a great temptation, as Amulek had given up all his earthly possessions when he had embraced the church.

In a powerful reply Amulek bore both testimony and rebuke:

> Now Amulek said: O thou child of hell, why tempt ye me? Knowest thou that the righteous yieldeth to no such temptations?
>
> Believest thou that there is no God? I say unto you, Nay, thou knowest that there is a God, but thou lovest that lucre more than him.
>
> And now thou has lied before God unto me. . . . And now behold, for this great evil thou shalt have thy reward. (Alma 11:23-25.)

Zeezrom eventually returned to Sidom, where he learned that Alma and Amulek had been cast into prison. There Alma and Amulek had called upon God to deliver them. The prison walls "were rent in twain, so that they fell to the earth," and the lawyers, priests, teachers, and chief judge had been "slain by the fall thereof" (Alma 14:27). Alma and Amulek had come forth out of the prison, loosed from their bands, unhurt.

But Zeezrom, some distance away in Sidom, knew nothing about the miracle at the prison. Realizing that Alma and Amulek had spoken the truth,

> Zeezrom lay sick at Sidom, with a burning fever, which was caused by the great tribulations of his mind on account of his wickedness, for he supposed that Alma and Amulek were no more; and he supposed that they had been slain because of his iniquity. And this great sin, and his many other sins, did harrow up his mind until it did become exceedingly sore, having no deliverance; therefore he began to be scorched with a burning heat. (Alma 15:3.)

Learning at last that Alma and Amulek were not only safe, but were in Sidom, Zeezrom sent for them and asked that they heal him. Alma, listening to Zeezrom's testimony of Christ, took him by the hand and healed him according to his faith in Christ.

Referring to this incident, Elder Boyd K. Packer wrote of the powerful influence of the mind on the body:

> I recently asked a doctor of family medicine how much of his time was devoted purely to correcting physical disorders. He has a large practice, and after thoughtfully considering, he answered, "Not more than 20 percent. The rest of the time I seem to be working on problems that very much affect the physical well-being of my patients but do not originate in the body.
>
> "These physical disorders," the doctor concluded, "are merely symptoms of some other kind of trouble. . . ."
>
> There is another part of us, not so tangible, but quite as real as our physical body. This intangible part of us is described as mind, emotion, intellect, temperament, and many other things. Very seldom is it described as spiritual.
>
> But there is a spirit in man; to ignore it is to ignore reality. There are spiritual disorders, too, and spiritual diseases that can cause intense suffering.
>
> The body and the spirit of man are bound together. Often, very often, where there are disorders, it is very difficult to tell which is which.[10]

The mind and the spirit, then, can contribute to physical fitness, but can also play a part in illness. Elder Packer's doctor was right: a large percentage of all physical problems have emotional roots. Some researchers believe that as many as half of all patients who visit physicians have physical symptoms that are directly caused by emotions; others think the figure is as high as 90 to 95 percent. Mounting scientific evidence indicates that virtually every illness may be influenced for good or bad by our emotions and attitudes that include factors such as faith and hope.

Illnesses don't just happen to us. Many are caused by bacteria, viruses, fungi, or other microbes. But disease-causing organisms constantly surround us, so what determines whether we get sick when we're exposed to them? What determines our ability to resist disease?

The answer may seem almost revolutionary: what goes on inside our minds, our hearts, and our spirits appears to have tremendous impact on what happens to our bodies.

Can the way we think and feel really be responsible, at least in part, for disease? A growing amount of evidence indicates they can. Emotional stress doesn't *cause* disease; as mentioned, many diseases are caused by microorganisms, like bacteria and viruses. But emotional stress is an important factor that can make us more susceptible to disease. And there is a physiological reason why: the brain controls both specific emotions and specific hormone patterns, and our hormones affect our health.

Here's an example of what can happen: when a person is aggressive and anxious, the body releases too much norepinephrine and epinephrine. These hormones cause the arteries to get thick and the muscles in the blood vessels to tighten. The immediate result is high blood pressure. If aggression and anxiety are chronic, long-term excess of the resulting hormones can cause hypertension, stroke, or heart failure.

The very words we use to describe our emotions are revealing. One author put it this way:

> We feel emotions in our bodies. We "burn" with anger, "tremble" with fear, feel "choked up" with sadness; our "stomachs turn" with revulsion. Everyone tends to experience unpleasant emotions as unpleasant bodily symptoms and thus to feel physically distressed when emotionally distressed.[11]

Medical researchers are finding that emotions seem to be strongly linked to a range of chronic and degenerative diseases. Heart disease has been long associated with emotional stress. Seventeenth-century physician William Harvey, who first mapped the circulatory system, noted that "every affliction of the mind that is attended with pain, pleasure, hope, or fear is the cause of an agitation whose influence extends to the heart." Extreme emotions in people with normal hearts can disturb heart rhythm; if people already have some kind of heart disease, extreme emotions can be fatal. In fact, comprehensive research shows that the most common factor in sudden cardiac death is a flood of strong emotion.

Physical illness has been linked to emotion in many scientific studies. Emotions can even play a role in the development of infectious diseases, those that are caused by identifiable microorganisms such as bacteria or viruses and that can be passed from one person to another. Our emotions can determine in part how susceptible we are, and whether those infectious agents will actually make us sick.

Excellent examples of this are cold sores and fever blisters, which are caused by the herpes simplex virus. Although the virus lives around the nose and mouth of most adults at all times, most of the time it doesn't cause sores. But the virus does flare up in certain conditions, and emotional upset is the most common factor that precedes an attack of cold sores.

Emotions and cold sores are so strongly linked that one soldier stationed at California's Fort MacArthur could accurately predict when he would break out in cold sores. Whenever he felt hostile emotions, he knew he would soon break out in cold sores. Then he made a remarkable discovery: if he channeled his hostility into something else, such as reading, he could prevent the sores from erupting.[12]

Can any of us gain the type of control shown by this soldier, who redirected feelings of hostility into a more productive activity? In this, as in all other spheres, we were given a perfect example by the Savior. "The most inspiring thing about the life of Jesus was not his ability to quiet the storm or control the tempest," said Elder Sterling W. Sill, "but his absolute control of himself. . . . Before we can be successful in our God-given dominion, our emotions must be brought under the direction of the spirit."[13]

Such a pursuit, says Elder Neal A. Maxwell, must begin with careful monitoring of what we allow to enter our thoughts and emotions. "The human mind is remarkably retentive," he teaches. "We must be careful of what we allow in our mind, for it will be there for a long time, reasserting itself at those very times when we may be most vulnerable. Just as harmful chemicals heedlessly dumped in a vacant lot can later prove lethal, so toxic thoughts and the mulching of the wrong memories in a vacant corner of the mind also take their toll."[14]

One of the reasons strong negative emotions can cause illness, even infectious disease, is that they may over time disrupt the immune system, the surveillance system created to defend our bodies against disease. When we experience strong emotions, the internal organs respond by preparing to flee or strike out (the classic "fight or flight response" of stress). Hormones speed through the bloodstream and send messages back to the nervous system.

Sometimes immediately, but more often gradually, these messages wear down the immune system. How? Scientific evidence shows that emotions send chemical messages to the brain; in response, the brain changes the way the body responds. The result may change the way the immune system responds to messages from the brain.

If negative emotions play a role, what about positive emotions? They, too, have a powerful effect on immunity. In fact, in an exciting study reported at the annual meeting of the Society for Behavioral Medicine, psychologist Arthur Stone of the State University of New York Medical School tracked a hundred men for three months. They found that both stress and pleasure had an effect on the immune system. But stress weakens the immune system for only one day. Positive emotions and pleasurable events, on the other hand, *strengthen* the immune system for *two days*. Perhaps the Psalmist said it best: "Pleasant words [are as] an honeycomb, sweet to the soul, and health to the bones" (Proverbs 16:24).

Does all this mean we should never have negative emotions? That we must banish anger and resentment and hostility, and fill our lives only with love and happiness? No. Such an existence is impossible. Even the Father and his Son have on occasion expressed righteous anger. The key lies not in which emotions seize us, but in how we react to them.

Rachel Naomi Remen is an accomplished physician who has battled a chronic disease for thirty-five years. Her private practice has focused on behavioral medicine, and she works primarily with those facing chronic illness. During a conference sponsored by the Institute for the Advancement of Health, she told her colleagues that the notion of "negative" emotions is disturbing—perhaps even dangerous.

At best, she says, "it implies that there is a way to live, a certain set of attitudes, that may guarantee survival." At worst, she says, "it may degenerate into self-tyranny and may lead the individual into some kind of mind control. Many people now seem to fear harboring 'negative' or 'wrong' thoughts in the same way people used to fear having evil thoughts."

According to Remen, the issue is deeper than simply experiencing a negative emotion. Her advice is profound: "Perhaps there is a positive way to feel *all* emotions. It seems to me that all emotions serve a purpose and are potentially life affirming. Perhaps it is not so much the emotions themselves as the way we deal with them that either is or is not life affirming."[15]

Remen points out that every physician has worked with loving, cheerful people who have died, grieving people who lived, angry people who never became ill, and humorous people who were unable to heal themselves. "So we have a mystery," she suggests—a mystery that will only be solved by more research and more sophisticated tools with which to conduct that research.

"We can learn that at the center of our agency is our freedom to form a healthy attitude toward whatever circumstances we are placed in!" writes Elder Neal A. Maxwell. "Those, for instance, who stretch themselves in service—though laced with limiting diseases—are often the healthiest among us. The Spirit can drive the flesh beyond where the body first agrees to go!"[16]

Indeed, there is still far to go. The knowledge we have so far is exciting, full of promise for the prospect of a whole new horizon on how we look at and treat disease—and, most important, how we might prevent it.

Regardless of present age and circumstance, "you are building your life," admonished President Spencer W. Kimball. "It will be cheap and shoddy or it will be valuable and beautiful; it will be full of constructive activities or it can be destructive; it can be full of joy and happiness, or it can be full of misery." What makes the difference? According to President Kimball, the determining factor is attitude: how far we climb depends on our attitude and response to each situation.[17]

"Attitude is an important part of the foundation upon which we build a productive life," counseled Elder M. Russell Ballard. "A good attitude produces good results, a fair attitude fair results, a poor attitude poor results. We each shape our own life, and the shape of it is determined largely by our attitude."[18]

Our attitude, in turn, is determined largely by our spirit. Though our lives are engineered by our own efforts, we walk by faith. The world may bid us to wait passively for some good thing to happen; the spirit, counseled Elder Joseph B. Wirthlin, bids us to persevere—refuses to let us give in to temptations, frustrations, disappointments, or discouragements.[19] "Our task," said President Thomas S. Monson, "is to become our best selves. One of God's greatest gifts to us is the joy of trying again, for no failure ever need be final."[20]

Elder Boyd K. Packer relates the power of the spirit in forming our attitudes:

> It was meant to be that life would be a challenge. To suffer some anxiety, some depression, some disappointment, even some failure is normal.
>
> . . . [If you] have a good, miserable day once in a while, or several in a row, stand steady and face them. Things will straighten out.
>
> There is great purpose in our struggle in life.[21]

The spirit tells us, as President James E. Faust has said, that "there is a divine purpose in the adversities we encounter every day. They prepare, they purge, they purify, and thus they bless."[22] The things of the spirit—faith, prayer, fasting, obedience, service, selflessness—confirm the truth of our mission in mortality and allow us the attitudes of eternal perspective.

President Hugh B. Brown asked each of us to imagine we are standing before a white canvas that represents our time in mortality. In one hand we clutch a set of brushes. We are charged with creating a masterpiece, and the paints we must use are our own thoughts, emotions, and conduct. They are determined in large part by our spirit. There is a wide variety to choose from, and the picture we paint will depend on how discriminating we are as we choose our "colors."

"We will achieve either harmony or discord," President Brown explained, "and as we work on the canvas, we have a vision in our minds and our creative imagination impels us to higher achievement." We see ourselves as the men and women we want to be. We work with considerable freedom. Each stroke of the brush, he added, leaves a lasting mark on the canvas of time. Each color—every emotion we feel, every thought we ponder, every way we react—will either "mar the painting or add to its beauty."[23]

We know, too, that each color and each stroke of the brush will help determine our health and wellness, thanks to the intimate connection between spirit, mind, and body.

END NOTES

1. David O. McKay, *Gospel Ideals*, comp. by G. Homer Durham (Salt Lake City: The Improvement Era, 1953), p. 394.

2. Daniel H. Ludlow, ed. *The Encyclopedia of Mormonism,* Vol. 3 (New York: Macmillan Publishers, 1992) p. 140.

3. Bruce R. McConkie, *Mormon Doctrine,* 2nd edition, revised (Salt Lake City: Bookcraft, 1966), p. 501.

4. Ibid.

5. Hugh Nibley, *Approaching Zion: The Collected Works of Hugh Nibley,* Volume 9 (Salt Lake City: Deseret Book, and Provo, Utah: The Foundation for Ancient Research and Mormon Studies, 1989), p. 304.

6. John Taylor, *The Government of God* (Liverpool, England: S. W. Richards, 1952), Chapter 9.

7. Joseph Fielding Smith, ed., *Teachings of the Prophet Joseph Smith* (Salt Lake City: Deseret Book, 1976), p. 181.

8. Ezra Taft Benson, *Teachings of Ezra Taft Benson* (Salt Lake City: Bookcraft, 1988), p. 480.
9. Ezra Taft Benson, "Your Charge: To Increase in Wisdom and Favor with God and Man," *New Era,* September 1979, p. 45.
10. Boyd K. Packer, "The Balm of Gilead," *Ensign,* November 1977, p. 59.
11. Arthur J. Barsky, *Worried Sick: Our Troubled Quest for Wellness* (Boston: Little, Brown, and Company, 1988), p. 62.
12. Herbert Benson, *The Mind/Body Effect* (New York: Simon and Schuster, 1979), p. 42.
13. Sterling W. Sill, *Conference Report,* October 1963, p. 78.
14. Neal A. Maxwell, *We Will Prove Them Herewith* (Salt Lake City: Deseret Book, 1982), p. 44.
15. Rachel Naomi Remen, "Feeling Well: A Clinician's Casebook," *Advances* 6:2, pp. 43-49.
16. Neal A. Maxwell, *Deposition of a Disciple* (Salt Lake City: Deseret Book, 1976), pp. 30-31.
17. Spencer W. Kimball, *Teachings of Spencer W. Kimball,* comp. by Edward L. Kimball (Salt Lake City: Bookcraft, 1982), p. 161.
18. M. Russell Ballard, "Providing for Our Needs," *Ensign,* May 1981, p. 86.
19. Joseph B. Wirthlin, "Never Give Up," *Ensign,* November 1987, pp. 8-10.
20. Thomas S. Monson, "The Will Within," *Ensign,* May 1987, p. 68.
21. Boyd K. Packer, *Conference Report,* April 1978, p. 140.
22. James E. Faust, *Conference Report,* April 1979, p. 79.
23. Hugh B. Brown, *The Abundant Life* (Salt Lake City: Bookcraft, 1965), p. 229.

To be truly fit, truly equal to the demands of life, requires much more than bodily strength. It involves the mind and the training of the mind, the emotions and their use and control. . . . the soul and the spiritual growth, too.

— EZRA TAFT BENSON

Bones can be straightened, germs can be killed, sutures can close wounds and skillful fingers can open and close bodies; but no man yet has found a way to actually heal. Man is the offspring of God and has within him the re-creating power that is God-given.

— Spencer W. Kimball

CHAPTER

2

THE MIND AND IMMUNITY

The *Encyclopedia of Mormonism*, in proclaiming that the upkeep and maintenance of the body are important in LDS belief, describes disease as "a natural condition that disturbs the normal function of the body's physical processes."[1]

The *Encyclopedia* then goes on to describe how members of The Church of Jesus Christ of Latter-day Saints deal with that physiological disruption:

> When ill or injured, Latter-day Saints exercise faith toward recovery. Worthy priesthood holders, by administering a blessing of health, may call upon the power of God to aid in the healing process. At the same time, Latter-day Saints are encouraged to take full advantage of modern medicine and technology in the prevention and cure of sickness and do not find this inconsistent with accepting the blessings of the priesthood, for they see an ultimate unity between spirit and matter.[2]

That "ultimate unity between spirit and matter"—the indisputable connection between the body and the spirit—works hand-in-hand with the power of the priesthood to bring about healing. The faith and priesthood power that attend such blessings, taught President Spencer W. Kimball, combine with prayer to "speed and encourage" the body's healing power.

Priesthood blessing "activates the body's own healing power," President Kimball continued. "It must be remembered that no physician can heal. He can only provide a satisfactory environment and situation so that the body may use its own God-given power of re-creation to build itself. . . . Man is the offspring of God and has within him the re-creating power that is God-given."[3]

Elder Malcolm S. Jeppsen, a practicing physician for more than forty years and then a member of the Seventy, said at the April 1994 general conference that

> physicians do not cure patients. This marvelous and complicated machine we call the human body has built into it its own wonderful healing mechanism. All a physician can do is provide a good healing environment. I soon learned in my medical practice that the ultimate healing process for an injured or sick body was already provided by our Heavenly Father. I also learned that a patient's attitude has much to do with healing. Those who would rely on Heavenly Father and exercise faith in the power of the priesthood often enjoyed faster recoveries.[4]

We know, as President Joseph Fielding Smith taught, that "the Lord works in accordance with natural law."[5] How, then, might the Lord employ natural law to bring about healing? Perhaps part of man's God-given re-creating power, mobilized by faith and the power of the priesthood, is the body's total immune system, our arsenal against disease.

If we want to understand how the mind and spirit can profoundly affect health, it's important to understand a little about immunity. As created by the Father, the body's first line of defense against disease is the immune system. It patrols and guards against attackers both from inside and outside the body. One of the body's most complicated systems, it consists of about a trillion cells called *lymphocytes* and about a hundred million trillion molecules called *antibodies*.

The complexity of the immune system is but one of the aspects of the body that bears silent testimony to a divine creator. The lymphocytes, or white blood cells—called *T-cells* and *B-cells*—are the key components of the immune system. They are produced in organs scattered throughout the body, including the bone marrow, tonsils, appendix, spleen, thymus, Peyer's patches (found in the small intestine), and the lymph nodes. Some of the lymphocytes (called "helper cells") stimulate the immune response; others (called "suppressor cells") turn it back off.

Still other lymphocytes are called *natural killer cells.* As their name implies, they attack and destroy other cells. Most normal cells resist attack by natural killer cells; mainly, natural killer cells destroy tumor cells or normal cells infected with a virus. The natural killer cells provide the greatest protection against cancer as they hunt down and destroy cells that develop abnormal changes.

Lymphocytes are also responsible for "acquired immunity"—the process that happens after an immunization or vaccination. Five hundred years before Christ was born, Greek physicians noticed that people who recovered from the plague never got it again. They had developed acquired immunity, though that's not what the Greeks called it. In essence, when exposed to some foreign invaders ("antigens"), certain kinds of lymphocytes become specialized "memory" cells. The next time these cells encounter the same antigen, they are primed to destroy it. The microorganisms in vaccines have been altered so they produce an immune response but do not cause full-blown disease.

Most of the time, the immune system works as it should; unfortunately, certain factors make it less effective. For example, studies show that the immune system weakens as we age. The thymus, a gland that produces disease-fighting lymphocytes, loses approximately 75 percent of its size and function by the age of twenty; by the age of sixty, it is virtually gone. Aging also upsets the balance between helper and suppressor cells; as a result, the immune response is turned off.

The immune system can also be suppressed by cancer and damaged by the drugs and radiation therapy used to treat cancer. Cells of the immune system itself may become malignant, resulting in diseases like lymphoma or leukemia. Certain congenital diseases or viral diseases (such as AIDS) can cause failures in the immune system, resulting in overwhelming infections and cancers. These immune system failures are called *immunodeficiency diseases.*

The immune system can also malfunction, developing a serious overreaction to substances that are usually harmless—pollen, animal dander, dust, or mildew, for example. The result is an allergic reaction. In some cases, the immune system becomes unbalanced and reacts to normal body tissues as though they were invaders; simply stated, the body becomes allergic to itself. The resulting diseases, such as rheumatoid arthritis and systemic lupus erythematosus, are called *autoimmune diseases.*

Finally, attitudes and emotions generated by the mind and the spirit can also affect the immune system. One of the most startling examples happened in 1975, when psychologist Robert Ader wanted to condition mice to avoid the artificial sweetener saccharin. To do it, he simultaneously fed the mice saccharin and injected them with a drug that caused upset stomach. Incidentally, the drug also suppressed the immune system. Associating the taste of saccharin with stomach pain, the mice soon learned to avoid the artificial sweetener.

Ader then decided to try to reverse the results. He gave the mice saccharin *without* the drug that caused the upset stomach to see if he could condition the mice to once again enjoy the taste of saccharin. He was surprised to find that the mice who had received the most saccharin during the first experiment *died* when they received saccharin during the second experiment.

What had happened? Ader speculated that he had so successfully conditioned the mice that just the taste of saccharin now weakened their immune systems enough to kill them.[6] This underscores the relationship between the immune system and the brain.

Our understanding of the brain has taken quantum leaps over the ages. Five centuries before the birth of Christ, the Greeks knew the brain simply as a three-pound organ inside the head. Hippocrates thought the brain cooled the blood and secreted mucus, which, of course, then flowed down through the nose. During the Middle Ages, scientists regarded the brain as the seat of the soul. With the gradual evolution of sophisticated scientific experiments, our ability to measure and analyze the electrical activity of the brain has helped us understand its function quite clearly.

Consider how privileged the brain is. It has a heart to supply it with blood and lungs to supply it with oxygen. It has intestines to provide it with nutrients, and kidneys to remove poisons from its environment. But all of that is of supreme importance: if the body is to survive, the brain must be maintained. All other organs of the body will sacrifice to keep the brain alive and functioning when the entire body is under severe stress.

The nerves that branch out from the brain and spinal cord lead to the sensory organs, such as the eyes, ears, and nose. Through these nerves we interpret the things we see, hear, and smell. Nerves also branch from the brain and spinal cord to the muscles, skin, and all organs of the body.

The brain masterminds the impulses that are carried along the nerves, sending information to various parts of the body. It controls the direction, strength, and coordination of muscle movements; the processes involved in touch, sight, and smell; and other processes over which we have conscious control. It also controls many of the functions in the body over which we have no conscious control, such as breathing, digestion, blood pressure, the rate of the heartbeat, and the release of hormones.

Finally, through its inexplicable link to the spirit, the brain is the place where ideas are generated, memory is stored, and emotions are experienced. As such, the brain has a powerful influence over the body—and a profound impact on the immune system.

Every time the brain/spirit experiences an emotion, that emotion is accompanied by physical responses. An article in *U.S. News and World Report* presents a vivid picture of what happens when feelings and physical responses combine:

> Seeing a shadow flit across your path in a dimly lit parking lot will trigger a complex series of events. First, sensory receptors in the retina of your eye detect the shadow and instantly translate it into chemical signals that race to your brain. Different parts of the limbic system [nerve pathways] and higher brain centers debate the shadow's importance. What is it? Have we encountered something like this before? Is it dangerous? Meanwhile, signals sent by the hypothalamus to the pituitary gland trigger a flood of hormones alerting various parts of your body to the possibility of danger, and producing the response called "fight or flight": Rapid pulse, rising blood pressure, dilated pupils, and other physiological shifts that prepare you for action. Hormone signals are carried through the blood, a much slower route than nerve pathways. So even after the danger is past—when your brain decides that the shadow is a cat's, not a mugger's—it takes a few minutes for everything to return to normal.[7]

That's what happens with fear, which is a relatively uncomplicated emotion. It's much more difficult to trace what happens with more complicated emotions, such as deep remorse or joy, but they are just as responsible for physical effects in the body.

Sophisticated research has shown an actual, biological connection between the brain and the immune system. More than three decades ago, Soviet researchers discovered they could change how the immune system worked by selectively damaging different parts of the brain. Carrying that research a step further, French scientists discovered that different sides of the brain control different immune system functions.

There are also physical links between the brain and the immune system over the intricate network of nerves. For example, the thymus produces immune system cells. Researchers have discovered extensive networks of nerve endings laced throughout the thymus, linking it directly to the brain.[8] Rich supplies of nerves also serve the spleen, bone marrow, and lymph nodes, giving further evidence to a physical link between the brain and the immune system.

Immune system cells are also specially equipped to respond to chemical signals from the brain and central nervous system. National Institute of Mental Health researchers found that certain white blood cells are equipped with what equates to "antennas tuned specifically to receive messages from the brain."[9]

Those messages from the brain come in the form of various chemicals and hormones, such as the growth hormone and the sex hormones. They also include the mix of hormones that surge through the bloodstream during stress—hormones like catecholamines and corticosteroids. Corticosteroids, in fact, are so effective in suppressing the immune system that they are widely used to treat allergic conditions (such as asthma and hay fever) and autoimmune disorders (such as rheumatoid arthritis).[10]

Still another brain chemical appears to have a profound influence on the immune system. *Endorphins* are the body's natural pain killers. Their ability to relieve pain has been compared to that of narcotic drugs, such as morphine. Endorphins also result in a sense of calm and well-being; they are, in fact, responsible for the well-known "runner's high." It may even be that endorphins flood the system in response to a spiritual inner peace.

The role of endorphins is apparently much more complex than originally thought. A report published in *Psychology Today* says that endorphins play a role in a potpourri of experiences—including, but not limited to, crying, laughing; getting thrills from music; experiencing stress or depression; eating chili peppers; compulsive gambling; physical stress such as performing aerobics or going through labor and delivery; feeling hunger; having a near-death experience; and feeling comfort from massage or playing with pets.[11]

The power of endorphins was demonstrated completely by accident when McGill University researcher James Olds was trying to condition an ordinary white rat to avoid one corner of its cage.[12] He knew that stimulation of a certain region of the brain called the *hypothalamus* is unpleasant, so he decided to sink an electrode into the rat's hypothalamus. Then he stimulated the electrode whenever the rat ventured into the corner of the cage. He figured the rat would soon avoid the corner of the cage.

To his surprise, the opposite thing happened: the rat developed a "compulsive fondness" for the corner of the cage, returning to it over and over. Olds was puzzled. Stimulation of the hypothalamus was supposed to be unpleasant; why, then, did the rat continue to do something that would result in unpleasant stimulation?

Then Olds discovered the reason: when he implanted the electrode, he missed his target—the hypothalamus—by a fraction of an inch. Instead, he had implanted the electrode in what would soon become known as the "pleasure center" of the brain: the center where endorphins are produced.

Olds next tried an experiment that allowed rats to stimulate the "pleasure center" themselves. Electrodes in the center of the brain were activated when the rats pressed a bar. The rats gave up everything—food, water, and even sex—in their pursuit of the bar. Some rats pressed the bar thousands of times, around the clock, until they dropped dead from starvation, thirst, or sheer exhaustion.

In moderate amounts, endorphins can kill pain, produce calm, and cause the thrill of anticipation. But too many endorphins can damage the immune system. For one thing, endorphins bind to the natural killer cells and make them less effective.

The connection of the brain to the immune system is just one example of the mind's ability to affect healing. Numerous scriptural examples, such as the Savior fasting for forty days, clearly demonstrate the power of the spirit over the body. Scientists have now shown that people can consciously control immune response by what they think. In one experiment, volunteers imagined their white blood cells to be strong, powerful sharks; immune system activity soared. In still another, patients were asked to use imagery to fight cancer; researchers found that the tumors grew or shrunk based on how specific, vivid, strong, and clear the patients' mental imagery was.[13]

Imagery can also be combined with traditional medical treatment to boost the immune system and enhance treatment, researchers say. In one study, researchers looked at 225 patients who had advanced cancer of the breast, bowel, or lung. The patients used imagery combined with the medical treatment traditionally used for their individual cancers, and they survived longer than the national average for people with those kinds of cancers. Researchers who compared survivors to those who had died determined that the survivors were more creative, more receptive to new ideas, more flexible, more argumentative, and expressed feelings of adequacy and vitality. When things started going downhill, they had turned to their inner resources.

One of the most important of those inner resources is faith. President Gordon B. Hinckley assures us, "God is weaving his tapestry according to his own grand design. All flesh is in his hands. We have no need to fear. We have no need to worry."[14]

Another important resource is the power of the priesthood—the authority to represent God the Father and to assist the Savior in bringing about the eternal life of men. President Spencer W. Kimball defined the priesthood as "the power that the Lord has given to us to do his will and to do his works."[15] As Elder Charles W. Penrose told early Church members, the priesthood "is a reality and not a mere name; it is not a mere calling in word, but an office which confers upon us power and influence that comes from the Almighty. . . . There is force in it, there is power and salvation in it."[16]

President N. Eldon Tanner once wrote, "The priesthood is for the blessing of all—men, women, and children. . . . By the power of the priesthood the sick are healed, the lame made to walk, the blind to see, and the deaf to hear, according to their faith and the will of our Father in heaven."[17]

That last caveat is an important one. Physical healing and sustaining of life may be our will, but not our Father's. Elder Malcolm S. Jeppsen pointed out the importance of recognizing the Lord's will when he said:

> The Lord has given a condition for healing blessings: "He that hath faith in me to be healed, *and is not appointed unto death*, shall be healed." (D&C 42:48; italics added.) Even

> when a person relies on faith in the Lord for blessings, if it is his or her appointed time to die, there will not be restoration of health. Indeed, "death [must come] upon all men, to fulfil the merciful plan of the great Creator." (2 Nephi 9:6.)[18]

Speaking of the willingness to heed the will of the Lord, President Marion G. Romney said:

> When we pray unto the Father in the name of Jesus for specific . . . things, we should feel in the very depths of our souls that we are willing to subject our petitions to the will of our Father in heaven. "Thy will, O God, thy will be done" should never be lip service only. "Thy will be done on earth as it is in heaven" (3 Nephi 13:10) is the pattern given by Jesus in the Lord's prayer, and emphasized in Gethsemane when in blood-sweat and agony he prayed, ". . . Not my will, but thine, be done." (Luke 22:42.)[19]

Indeed, as President Spencer W. Kimball pointed out, if "all the sick for whom we pray were healed, if all the righteous were protected and the wicked destroyed, the whole program of the Father would be annulled. . . . There would be little or no suffering, sorrow, disappointment, or even death, and if these were not, there would also be no joy, success, resurrection, nor eternal life."[20]

Created after the image of a divine Father, the human body can be conceived of as a self-healer, endowed with an internal supply of chemicals and hormones that "maintain and enhance health."[21] Activated by the power of the priesthood, the immune system can heal. The spirit can mobilize the body as it absorbs the lessons of mortality. As Elder Orson F. Whitney told early members of the Church:

> No pain that we suffer, no trial that we experience is wasted. It ministers to our education, to the development of such qualities as patience, faith, fortitude, and humility. All that we suffer and all that we endure, especially when we endure

> it patiently, builds up our characters, purifies our hearts, expands our souls, and makes us more tender and charitable, more worthy to be called the children of God.[22]

END NOTES

1. Daniel H. Ludlow, ed., *The Encyclopedia of Mormonism,* Volume 3 (New York: Macmillan Publishers, 1992), p. 129.
2. Ibid.
3. Spencer W. Kimball, *The Teachings of Spencer W. Kimball,* comp. by Edward L. Kimball (Salt Lake City: Bookcraft, 1982), p. 508.
4. Malcolm S. Jeppsen, "A Divine Prescription for Spiritual Healing," *Ensign,* May 1994, p. 17.
5. Joseph Fielding Smith, *Doctrines of Salvation: Sermons and Writings of Joseph Fielding Smith,* Bruce R. McConkie, ed. (Salt Lake City: Bookcraft, 1955), Volume 2, p. 27.
6. Stephen S. Hall, "A Molecular Code Links Emotions, Mind, and Health," *Smithsonian,* June 1989, pp. 68-72.
7. Erica E. Goode, "Accounting for Emotion," *U.S. News and World Report,* June 27, 1988, p. 53.
8. Larry Dossey, *Healing Words* (San Francisco: Harper San Francisco, 1993), pp. 105-106.
9. Shannon Brownlee, "The Body at War," *U.S. News and World Report,* July 2, 1990, pp. 48-54.
10. *Ibid.*
11. Janet L. Hopson, "A Pleasurable Chemistry," *Psychology Today,* July/August 1988, p. 29.
12. Judith Hooper, "The Brain's River of Rewards," *American Health,* December 1987, p. 38.
13. Larry Dossey, *Healing Words* (San Francisco: Harper San Francisco, 1993), p. 105.
14. Gordon B. Hinckley, *Conference Report,* April 1983, p. 5.
15. In *Philippine Islands Area Conference Report,* August 1975, p. 30.
16. *Deseret News Weekly,* April 21, 1880, p. 178.
17. N. Eldon Tanner, "The Priesthood of God," *Ensign,* June 1973, p. 6.

18. Malcolm S. Jeppsen, "A Divine Prescription for Spiritual Healing, *Ensign*, May 1994, p. 17.
19. Marion G. Romney, *Conference Report*, October 1944, p. 55.
20. Spencer W. Kimball, *Faith Precedes the Miracle* (Salt Lake City: Deseret Book, 1972), p. 97.
21. Maureen Groër, "Psychoneuroimmunology," *American Journal of Nursing*, August 1991, p. 33.
22. Orson F. Whitney, quoted in Spencer W. Kimball, *Faith Precedes the Miracle* (Salt Lake City: Deseret Book, 1975), p. 98.

No physician can heal. He can only provide a satisfactory environment and situation so that the body may use its own God-given power of re-creation to build itself.

— SPENCER W. KIMBALL

Men's and nations' finest hours consist of those moments when extraordinary challenge is met by extraordinary response. Hence in those darkest hours, we must light our individual candles rather than vying with others to call attention to the enveloping darkness.

— NEAL A. MAXWELL

CHAPTER

3

The Disease-Resistant Personality

Too often we ask ourselves why someone becomes ill. When twenty-five people are exposed to the flu virus, science rushes in to study the five who get sick. Perhaps, instead, we should focus even more effort in studying the twenty who didn't get sick.[1] We need to determine how it is that some manage to stay well—some in spite of the bleakest circumstances and the most daunting stresses.

We know that stress makes people ill. Biologist and neuroscientist Robert M. Sapolsky of Stanford Medical School points out that

> as recently as 1900, the leading causes of death in America were tuberculosis, pneumonia, and flu. In just a few generations, we have conquered these and nearly all other infectious diseases, as well as those of poor hygiene and undernutrition. Suddenly, Americans live and die differently from any other humans in history and most other people on Earth. Instead of succumbing to childhood infection, or passing away in one night's malarial fever, we now survive long enough to witness the slow deterioration of our bodies—the steady clogging of arteries, the gradual

> weakening of the immune system until it finally lets the seed of a tumor take root. One of the most important medical insights of recent decades has been that these diseases of aging—and the pace at which they advance—can be greatly affected by how we lead our lives, in particular, by how much stress we experience.[2]

Few of us can completely control how much stress we experience. And all of us will experience adversity. But some apparently *can* control whether the stress makes them ill. As President Marion G. Romney related, "I have seen the remorse and despair in the lives of men who, in the hour of trial, have cursed God and died spiritually. And I have seen people rise to great heights from what seemed to be unbearable burdens."[3]

Many remember the quiet morning of June 5, 1976, when the Teton Dam in southeastern Idaho broke, sending a raging wall of destruction through the area around the town of Rexburg. Entire communities were destroyed; businesses, farms, and homes were swept away by more than 250,000 acre-feet of water. More than seven thousand people lost everything they owned. Visiting the site not long after the flood, Elder Boyd K. Packer challenged the Saints: "Fine people, living worthily, can be subject to disasters such as you have faced here. The difference will be in how you face it."[4]

How we face things depends to a large extent on our personality. *Personality* is the sum of the personal characteristics, behavioral qualities, and emotional tendencies that make up each individual. It is the combination of habits, attitudes, and traits that make each person unique. Personality is determined by spirit and is dependent upon the qualities and experiences we bring with us from the pre-existence. It is the pattern of behavior that distinguishes each person from all other people.[5]

Personality is powerfully shaped by the family, the environment, and culture. However, personality is also partially determined by genetics and biology—by the unique set of genes each person inherits at birth. We also know that personality is influenced by the individual tendencies we brought as intelligences to our spirit birth and, later, by the strength and degree to which we developed during our premortal life. According to Elder Neal A. Maxwell, a true picture of the human personality and how it has been shaped can emerge only when we consider that premortal experience along with the influence of genetics and environment.[6]

We know, too, that personality endures—that, just as it existed in our premortal condition, it will continue after this life ends. President David O. McKay wrote:

> In what, then, does true immortality consist? It consists in the persistence of personality after death. The Savior's heartbeats were silenced, his body placed in the tomb; but his personality, the eternal part, lived and moved and had its being in the eternal beyond. . . . Eighteen hundred years later that Being appeared to the Prophet Joseph Smith, personally—not just in a dream, not in imagination, but in reality. . . . Personality is persistent, and that is the message of comfort, that is the real way in which death is conquered. Death cannot touch the spirit of man.[7]

If we know that personality existed before our physical body was created, and that our personality does not end with death, it stands to reason that our personality is much more powerful than the flesh. Logic would tell us, then, that personality has a forceful influence on health—a notion that has been observed for centuries and is being proved today with a flood of scientific data. Now follow that line of reasoning to its commanding conclusion: *changing* certain personality traits may allow us to change our health.

People who are resilient, who are able to withstand life's stresses without becoming ill, have developed certain personality traits and patterns of thinking that protect them in otherwise devastating situations. President Spencer W. Kimball quoted historian James Allen to demonstrate the power we can have over life's circumstances:

> Circumstance does not make the man; it reveals him to himself. . . . Man, as the lord and master of his thoughts, is

> the maker of himself, the shaper and author of environment. . . . Let a man radically alter his thoughts, and he will be astonished at the rapid transformation it will effect in the material conditions of his life.[8]

Some *can* stay well, because they have learned to control how they react. In a very real sense, they have become the authors of their environment. These resilient people are what Indiana psychiatric social worker Katherine Northcraft calls *transcenders*—people who, "in the worst of times, envision themselves as elsewhere, imagining that they can do great things despite their surroundings."[9] They are like the Prophet Joseph Smith—who, while languishing in Liberty Jail, looked toward heaven and received some of the most profound revelation in modern-day scripture. They somehow sensed their own worth. They were the kind of people described by historian James Allen:

> He who cherishes a beautiful vision, a lofty ideal in his heart, will one day realize it. Columbus cherished a vision of another world, and he discovered it; Copernicus fostered the vision of a multiplicity of worlds and a wider universe, and he revealed it; Buddha beheld the vision of a spiritual world of stainless beauty and perfect peace, and he entered into it.[10]

Psychologist Suzanne Ouellette Kobasa became keenly interested in people who, while exposed to intense or unrelenting stress, sailed through without getting sick. After years of study, she launched one study that changed forever the way scientists regarded our ability to resist stress.

For her study, Kobasa chose two hundred of the most stressed middle- and upper-level executives at Illinois Bell. At the time, the company was being dashed by the AT&T divestiture. Many executives were experiencing a change in responsibilities. Some were likely to lose their jobs completely. Worst of all, no one knew for sure how things would eventually settle.

Half of the executives in the study got sick from the stress. But Kobasa was much more interested in the other half—the ones who were under the same stresses but *who didn't get sick.*

She found that the healthy executives "were not younger, wealthier, higher on the career ladder, or better-educated than their colleagues who became sick under stress."[11] But the healthy executives did share a unique set of personality traits that determined how they dealt with stress. Kobasa called it "hardiness." The study convinced her—and scores of researchers after her—that the key to wellness is a different way of looking at and dealing with stressful events.[12]

Hardiness is "a set of beliefs about oneself, the world, and how they interact. It takes shape as a sense of personal commitment to what you are doing, a sense of control over your life, and a feeling of challenge."[13] We as Latter-day Saints know it as the deep conviction inspired by the plan of salvation: the knowledge of who we are, where we came from, what we are doing here, and where we are going. Kobasa defines it simply as "the three Cs"—*commitment* (an attitude of curiosity and involvement), *challenge* (the belief that change is an opportunity, not a threat), and *control* (the belief that you can influence events).

COMMITMENT

Commitment—an attitude of curiosity and involvement in what is happening around us—means a commitment to ourselves, our religious values, our family, our work, and the other important things in our lives. It is not a fleeting involvement, but a deep and abiding interest. As Elder Neal A. Maxwell put it, once even a "trace of commitment occurs, then things begin to happen."[14]

People who are committed in this way have a deep involvement with their work and their families, a deep sense of meaning, and a pervasive sense of direction in their lives. The important element, say some researchers, is a commitment to an ideal greater than oneself.[15] For many of us, that comes in the form of commitment to gospel values. For many, it is a deep commitment to a Christ-like way of life. For others, it's a commitment to political reform or to a certain philosophy. And some have a deep sense of commitment to something as simple as a hobby.

A perfect example is Mohandas K. Gandhi, a man who by all standards was a driven workaholic. He went on countless fasts, depriving himself of nourishment, and spent months in prison—one of the most stressful scenarios possible. Yet he was strong and healthy until his assassination at the age of seventy-seven. Many believe his health was due to his unwavering commitment to win political freedom for his homeland.

CHALLENGE

Challenge means the ability to see change as an opportunity for growth and excitement, not as a threat. An unhealthy person approaches change with helplessness and alienation. A healthy, hardy person can face change with confidence, self-determination, eagerness, and excitement. University of Southern Colorado psychologist Joan C. Post-Gordon says that healthy people don't even *see* the negatives, because they thoroughly expect a positive outcome.

Elder Neal A. Maxwell tells of author Eric Hoffer, who recalled in *Ordeal of Change* his days as a migrant farm worker in California during the Depression. "He picked the peas," Elder Maxwell wrote. "As the crop ripened, Hoffer worked his way northward. When the peas were all picked, he was asked if he were interested in picking string beans. Hoffer's reasoning symbolizes, on a small, amusing scale, the real challenge of change that faces each of us: he said he knew he could pick peas but he was not sure he could pick string beans. The refusal of some of us to learn to 'pick string beans' inevitably blocks us from new growth experiences."[16]

President Spencer W. Kimball taught that "every normal person has the capacity, with God's help, to meet the challenge of whatever circumstances may confront him. One of the most comforting scriptures carries the message that God will not leave us helpless—ever."[17]

The challenges we face in mortality may seem like threats, but ultimately they contribute to our growth. Elder Richard G. Scott taught, "Challenge comes as a testing from a wise, knowing Father to give experience, that we may be seasoned, mature, and grow in understanding and application of His truths. When you are worthy, a challenge becomes a contribution to growth, not a barrier to it."[18]

And as Elder Hartman Rector, Jr., so wisely said, "The Master spoke of the 'second mile' and told us to go there. Why? Because he wants to bless us, and he put all the blessings in the second mile."[19]

CONTROL

Control is the belief that we can influence how negative an event will be. It's the belief that we can cushion the hurtful impact of a situation by the way we look at it and react to it. It's the opposite of helplessness, the refusal to be victimized. It is not the erroneous belief that we can control our environment, our circumstances, or other people; instead, it's the belief that we can control *ourselves* and *our own reactions* to what life hands us.

Each of us lies somewhere along a continuum when it comes to our sense of control. At one end of the continuum is the "external locus of control." People with an external locus of control believe things that happen to them are unrelated to their own behavior—and, subsequently, beyond their control.[20] They are like a boxer in the ring:

> When the stresses of life buffet them, they lay against the ropes of despair and wish that things would get better. They erroneously decide that their opponent, stress, is much too strong for them, so they don't even try to fight back. [They feel that] everything that happens to them is controlled by external forces and that their actions do not influence what happens to them. Like pawns in a chess game, [they] believe that they are randomly moved about by the players of "luck, chance, fate, or predestination."[21]

At the opposite end of the continuum are those with an internal locus of control. These individuals believe that negative events are a consequence of personal actions, and can thus be potentially controlled.[22] They "believe their own actions have a large influence on what happens to them. If they get fired from a job, [they] believe that when they go out to look for a job they will be able to find one. They do not give up; rather, they hope for a brighter future."[23] As researcher Phillip Rice so aptly put it, "If the theme song of the external is *Cast Your Fate to the Wind,* then the theme song of the internal is *I Did It My Way.*"[24]

Research shows that we can increase our sense of control by being informed, having a less pessimistic outlook, placing faith in someone or something we deeply trust, learning new coping skills, building a stronger support system, and being prepared. We can feel in control when we take personal responsibility. Elder Hugh W. Pinnock said, "It is entirely appropriate to depend on others for some of what we need. There is no substitute for loving and supportive parents, priesthood and auxiliary leaders, skilled doctors, dedicated teachers, and expert auto mechanics. Turning to these people for help is not wrong. But what is wrong is expecting others to do what we can and should do for ourselves."[25]

As we face our challenges, Elder Richard G. Scott counseled, "Don't say, 'No one understands me; I can't sort it out, or get the help I need.' Those comments are self-defeating. No one can help you without faith and effort on your part."[26]

Our own faith and effort depends partly on a strong sense of self. An old English weaver once prayed, "O God, help me to hold a high opinion of myself." Recalling that supplication, President Harold B. Lee said, "That should be the prayer of every soul; not an abnormally developed self-esteem that becomes haughtiness, conceit, or arrogance, but a righteous self-respect that might be defined as 'belief in one's worth, worth to God, and worth to man.'"[27] The self-esteem we seek, taught President James E. Faust, "is not blind, arrogant, vain love of self, but is self-respecting, unconceited, honest esteem of ourselves . . . born of inner peace and strength."[28]

Belief in our worth to God is the foundation for self-esteem. That belief brings special meaning to the sweet lyrics, "I am a child of God." Consider for a moment our heritage, as Elder Boyd K. Packer outlined it:

> You are a child of God. He is the father of your spirit. Spiritually you are of noble birth, the offspring of the King of Heaven. Fix that truth in your mind and hold to it. However many generations in your mortal ancestry, no matter what race or people you represent, the pedigree of your spirit can be written on a single line. You are a child of God![29]

How we feel about ourselves—our self-esteem—is powerful because it sets the boundaries for what we can and cannot do, what we can and cannot become. Simply, it is the blueprint for our behavior. Self-esteem even affects well-being. When we have a strong sense of self-esteem, we are somebody. We have some control, and that control influences our health, because it impacts the way we react to situations that cause stress. Strong self-esteem gives us a good outlook and helps protect our health.

An important part of self-esteem is what psychologists call *self-efficacy*: the belief in our ability to do a certain thing, the conviction that we can manage adverse events in our lives. Self-efficacy determines our level of effort; if we believe we can succeed, we keep on trying. Such confidence in our abilities endows us with perseverance in the face of failure: if we really believe in ourselves, we're less likely to give up. It determines, too, how we react to stress: we're not likely to get overwhelmed if we think our situation is manageable. According to Dr. Albert Bandura of Stanford University, "When beset with difficulties, people who entertain serious doubts about their capabilities slacken their efforts or give up altogether, whereas those who have a strong sense of efficacy exert great effort to master the challenges."[30]

One reason a sense of control has such a profound influence over health is that lack of control disturbs the precise balance of chemicals and hormones in the body. When we feel little sense of control, our body produces smaller amounts of serotonin, which regulates mood and relieves pain; dopamine, which lets us feel a sense of reward or pleasure; and norepinephrine, which helps prevent depression.[31] In addition, people with an external locus of control produce high levels of stress hormones that can cause significant physical damage. And research shows that people who feel powerless, helpless, and out of control generally have compromised immune function, but those who have a sense of control have healthier immune systems.

Former *Saturday Review* editor Norman Cousins, renowned for his work linking attitudes and health, maintains that, in general,

> anything that restores a sense of control to a patient can be a profound aid to a physician in treating serious illness. That sense of control is more than a mere mood or attitude, and may well be a vital pathway between the brain, the endocrine system, and the immune system. The assumed possibility is that it may serve as the basis for what may well be a profound advancement in the knowledge of how to confront the challenge of a serious illness.[32]

For us, a sense of control comes with deep faith. Because of our faith in the plan of salvation, we feel a sense of control over our eventual destiny and a sense of meaning in what happens to us in the meantime. President Spencer W. Kimball taught:

> We are sons and daughters of God, possessing seeds of godhood. We are not limited by instinct as are the beasts. We have godly power to grow and to overcome . . . our own backgrounds may have been frustrating, but as sons and daughters of a living God we have within ourselves the power to rise above our circumstances, to change our lives. Man can change human nature. . . . We can overcome. We must control and master ourselves.[33]

Satan, said Elder Richard G. Scott, wants us to feel out of control. He "would separate you from the power of the love of God, kindred, and friends that want to help. He would lead you to feel that the walls are pressing in around you and there is no escape or relief. He wants you to believe you lack the capacity to help yourself and that no one else is really interested."[34]

In conclusion, hardiness promotes health. People with the traits of a disease-resistant personality have fewer episodes of illness, even when people around them have contagious diseases. They may even heal more quickly when they do get sick. In fact, researchers have identified what they call a "self-healing personality"—and they say it's characterized by enthusiasm, alertness, responsiveness, energy, curiosity, security, and contentment. Scientists say "self-healing" people have a continual sense of growth and resilience; achieve balance in meeting their biological needs, gaining affection, and having self-respect; are good problem-solvers; have a playful sense of humor; and have good relationships with others.[35]

In all of our lives come seasons—just as nature itself is punctuated with seasons. Both those of plenty and those of adversity are necessary. In drawing the comparison between our lives and the example of nature, Elder Franklin D. Richards said:

> We have seasons of great outward prosperity and also those of apparent adversity—when everything appears to be at a standstill and even dead; nature itself declares it to be a necessary condition. After the husbandsman has sown his grain, nursed its growth and harvested the crop, behold, the sere and yellow leaf of autumn comes, the winter frosts freeze up the streams and all nature appears somber and sorrowful—quite a different state of things to that which was going on during the summer.
>
> It is [as] necessary for us to have cloudy weather and rainy weather, as it is that we should have sunshine, in order to bring about the objects of creation, the purposes of nature, and the best interests of the human family. Seeing it is so in temporal things, is it strange that we should be the same, or even more so, in spiritual things?[36]

In our own challenges, we are reminded of those who went before, of those whose example shows us the way to become resilient. As Elder Neal A. Maxwell wrote:

> Jesus' last hours and moments were the most cruel. His prophet, Joseph Smith, underwent last hours and moments that were not filled with serene surroundings. Carthage was, for a time, a corner of hell, filled with filthy conversation that vexed his soul. Some disciples do not end their soldierly and gallant journey in a vigorous salute in dress parade, but in halting senility or with a stroke that stretches out their days. What is God doing? What lessons are underway? We can only surmise and trust. If growth is tied to challenge—and it is—we must expect righteousness to meet resistance.[37]

There was no freedom from challenge for the Savior of this world, nor will there be freedom from challenge for us. We become resilient when we meet that challenge with a sense of eagerness and anticipation of growth. We need to know, too, as Elder Richard G. Scott so wisely counseled, that when we feel we can do no more, we can temporarily lay our challenges at his feet:

> Recognize that some challenges in life will not be resolved here on earth. . . . [The Lord] wants you to learn how to be cured when that is His will and how to obtain strength to live with your challenge when He intends it to be an instrument for growth. In either case the Redeemer will support you. That is why He said, "Take my yoke upon you, and learn of me; . . . For my yoke is easy, and my burden is light." (Matthew 11:29-30.)[38]

END NOTES

1. Evan G. Pattishall, "The Development of Behavioral Medicine: Historical Models," *Annals of Behavioral Medicine,* November 1989, pp. 43-48.

2. Robert M. Sapolsky, "Lessons of the Serengeti," *The Sciences,* May 1988, p. 38.

3. Marion G. Romney, *Conference Report,* October 1969, p. 69.

4. David Mitchell, "Thousands of Saints Left Homeless by Idaho Flood," *Ensign,* August 1976, p. 74.

5. Clive Wood, "Type-Casting: Is Disease Linked With Personality?" *Nursing Times,* Vol. 84, No. 48, 1988, p. 26.

6. Neal A. Maxwell, *Deposition of a Disciple* (Salt Lake City: Deseret Book, 1976), pp. 41- 42.

7. David O. McKay, *Gospel Ideals,* comp. by G. Homer Durham (Salt Lake City: The Improvement Era, 1953), pp. 54-55.

8. Spencer W. Kimball, *The Miracle of Forgiveness* (Salt Lake City: Bookcraft, 1969), p. 105.

9. Kenneth Pelletier, *Sound Mind, Sound Body: A New Model for Lifelong Health* (New York: Simon and Schuster, 1994), p. 57.

10. Spencer W. Kimball, *The Miracle of Forgiveness* (Salt Lake City: Bookcraft, 1969), pp. 105-106.

11. Suzanne Ouellette Kobasa, "How Much Stress Can You Survive?" *American Health,* September 1984, pp. 71-79.

12. Blair Justice, "Those Who Stay Healthy," *New Realities,* July/August 1988, pp. 35-39.

13. Joshua Fischman, "Getting Tough," *Psychology Today,* December 1987, pp. 26-28.

14. Neal A. Maxwell, *That My Family Should Partake* (Salt Lake City: Deseret Book, 1974), p. 44.

15. Howard S. Friedman, *The Self-Healing Personality* (New York: Henry Holt and Company, 1991), p. 110.

16. Neal A. Maxwell, *A More Excellent Way: Essays on Leadership for Latter-day Saints* (Salt Lake City: Deseret Book, 1910), p. 42.

17. Spencer W. Kimball, *The Teachings of Spencer W. Kimball,* comp. by

Edward L. Kimball (Salt Lake City: Bookcraft, 1982), p. 161.
18. Richard G. Scott, "To Be Healed," *Ensign,* May 1994, p. 9.
19. Hartman Rector, Jr., *Conference Report,* April 1979, p. 42.
20. H. M. Lefcourt, *Locus of Control: Current Trends in Theory and Research* (Hillsdale, N.J.: Erlbaum, 1976), p. 29.
21. S. I. McMillen, *None of These Diseases,* revised (Old Tappan, New Jersey: Fleming H. Revell Company, 1984), p. 177.
22. H. M. Lefcourt, *Locus of Control: Current Trends in Theory and Research* (Hillsdale, New Jersey: Erlbaum, 1976), p. 29.
23. S. I. McMillen, *None of These Diseases,* revised (Old Tappan, N.J.: Fleming H. Revell Company, 1984), pp. 177-78.
24. Phillip L. Rice, *Stress and Health* (Monterey, California: Brooks/Cole Publishing Company, 1987), p. 109.
25. Hugh W. Pinnock, *Conference Report,* April 1989, p. 12.
26. Richard G. Scott, "To Be Healed," *Ensign,* May 1994, p. 8.
27. Harold B. Lee, *Stand Ye In Holy Places: Selected Sermons and Writings of President Harold B. Lee* (Salt Lake City: Deseret Book, 1975), pp. 6-7.
28. James E. Faust, *Reach Up for the Light* (Salt Lake City: Deseret Book, 1990), p. 31.
29. Boyd K. Packer, "To Young Women and Men," *Ensign,* May 1989, p. 53.
30. Dr. Albert Bandura, "Self-Efficacy," *University of California Berkeley Wellness Letter,* Vol. 3, No. 8, 1987, pp. 1-2.
31. P. Ahluwalia, R. M. Zacharko, and H. Anisman, *Dopamine Variations Associated with Acute and Chronic Stressors,* Presentation at the Annual Meeting of the Society of Neuroscience, Dallas, Texas, 1992.
32. Norman Cousins, *Head First: The Biology of Hope* (New York: E. P. Dutton, 1989), p. 120.
33. Spencer W. Kimball, *Faith Precedes the Miracle* (Salt Lake City: Deseret Book, 1972), pp. 175-76.
34. Richard G. Scott, "To Be Healed," *Ensign,* May 1994, p. 8.
35. Howard S. Friedman and Gary R. VandenBos, "Disease-Prone and Self-Healing Personalities," *Hospital and Community Psychiatry,* Vol. 23, No. 12, 1992, p. 1178.
36. Brian H. Stuy, ed., *Collected Discourses* (Burbank, Calif., and Woodland Hills, Utah: BHS Publishing Company, 1987), Vol. 1.

37. Neal A. Maxwell, *Wherefore, Ye Must Press Forward* (Salt Lake City: Deseret Book, 1977), p. 125.
38. Richard G. Scott, "To Be Healed," *Ensign,* May 1994, p. 7.

By faith all things are possible; nothing is too hard for the Lord. No sickness is too severe, no disease too disabling, no plague too destructive to be cured by the power that is faith. Whether in life or in death nothing is withheld from those who abide the law of faith.

— Bruce R. McConkie

CHAPTER 4

The Healing Power of Faith

As he preached in an unnamed city near the shores of Galilee, Jesus was approached by a man the scriptures describe as "full of leprosy."

Few in today's industrialized nations have seen leprosy—a disease that Elder Bruce R. McConkie called "a living death," a condition that inspired "the most frightful images of suffering and degradation—corrupting as it did the very fountains of the life-blood of man, distorting his countenance, rendering loathsome his touch, slowly encrusting him and infecting him with a plague-spot of disease far more horrible than death itself."[1] The rabbis of the day taught that leprosy could not be cured. And it never has been. By Levitical law, no one was permitted to touch a person afflicted with leprosy; a single touch rendered one unclean.

The man who approached Jesus that day was in the last stages of leprosy. Scarcely an inch of his flesh had not been consumed by the dread disease. Certainly, death was imminent. But seeing Jesus, the man fell on his face in worship. As Elder James E. Talmage wrote, "The petition implied in the words of this poor creature was pathetic; the confidence he expressed is inspiring."[2] His voice rang clear: "Lord, if thou wilt, thou canst make me clean" (Matthew 8:2).

With no thought for his own health, the Master reached forth his hand and touched the leper, saying, "I will; be thou clean." And, the accounts say, "immediately his leprosy was cleansed" (Matthew 8:3). As Elder Bruce R. McConkie wrote, "his leprosy departs, and the miracle is wrought. Nothing is too hard for the Lord."[3]

But let's consider the leper himself: "Here is a man of faith," wrote Elder Bruce R. McConkie. "There is no question as to *whether* Jesus can heal him—only *will* the Great Healer use his power in this case. Indeed, here is a man of great faith, for it would take an almost unbounded spiritual assurance to have the confidence of a restoration of health from a disease so dread."[4] In fact, taught President Spencer W. Kimball, in most of Christ's healings, he credited the individual's faith rather than his own great power.[5]

Indeed, Jesus was the greatest teacher of faith. He healed the sick, restored sight to the blind, and even raised up the dead. But, more than that, he urged every soul touched by disease to exercise faith sufficient to bring about a healing. He taught that with faith, all things are possible. To the father who pleaded with Jesus to travel to Capernaum and heal his son, who "was at the point of death" (John 4:47), Jesus simply said, "Go thy way; thy son liveth" (John 4:50). And, we are told, the man believed; before he arrived home, he knew beyond a doubt that his son had been restored.

The father's rooted display of faith allowed not only his son's recovery, wrote Elder Bruce R. McConkie, but his own spiritual cure, enabling him to "shake off the disease of unbelief that leads to spiritual death." Speaking of the father, he taught that "the growth of faith in an earthbound pilgrim, and the healing, as it were, of the soul of man, is as great a miracle as—nay, a far greater miracle than—the healing of the physical body."[6]

What is faith? The Prophet Joseph Smith taught that it is a principle of power—and that, as such, it has dominion and authority over all things. It is, he said, the first principle of revealed religion and the foundation of all righteousness. President Ezra Taft Benson taught that faith is "the foundation upon which a godlike character is built. It is the prerequisite for all other virtues."[7]

Faith is the assurance we have of things not seen. As the resurrected Christ told the doubting Thomas Didymus, "Blessed are they that have not seen, and yet have believed" (John 20:29). The French novelist George Sand wrote that faith "is an excitement and an enthusiasm," a condition "of intellectual magnificence to which we must cling as a treasure, and not squander in the small coin of empty words." If the results of recent scientific studies are correct, faith is indeed a treasure—not only in the spiritual sense, but as a potent factor in both good health and healing.

Faith protects health and promotes healing by strengthening the body against the physical changes that can accompany stress. In the same way, it can even affect the course of disease. A review of studies confirms the power of faith over physiological processes;[8] faith has been shown to influence microbes, plants, animals, and human beings, even from a distance. These studies, combined with personal experiences, have resulted in a growing appreciation of faith among members of the medical community.

Faith can affect the healing process partly because of its power to convince. Research has clearly demonstrated that what exists is not as important as what we *believe* to exist. Personal belief gives us an unseen power that enables us to do the impossible, to perform miracles—even to heal ourselves.

Cardiologist Herbert Benson related a perfect example of the power of perceptions: movie audiences in air-conditioned theaters became extremely hot and thirsty while watching the classic epic *Lawrence of Arabia.* During intermissions, concession stands were inundated with people demanding ice-cold drinks in what Benson calls an "epidemic of thirst." People weren't being deprived of water, but they identified so thoroughly with the movie "that their bodies became 'convinced' they were on the Arabian dunes."[9] According to Benson, research "is demonstrating ever more clearly that the things we can touch, taste, and measure frequently have to take a back seat to what we *perceive or believe* to be real"; just having a strong belief is enough to cause things to happen to our bodies.[10]

That belief is what's behind "the placebo effect"—the physical change that occurs because of what we *think* a pill or procedure will do but that is *not* caused by the specific properties of the pill or the procedure itself. If a person deeply believes that a pill is going to work in a certain way, chances are that it will—even if the pill is made of nothing more than table sugar. A placebo doesn't necessarily need to be a pill; it can also be a potion, a surgical procedure, some other medical procedure, or even a physician.

In the case of a placebo, the healer is faith, not medication. Yale cancer specialist and surgeon Bernie Siegel claims that the placebo suggests "that we may be able to change what takes place in our bodies by changing our state of mind."[11]

A dramatic example of the placebo effect occurred in a New York hospital where women were being treated for severe pregnancy-related nausea and vomiting. Dr. Stewart Wolf told the women he was giving them a drug known to relieve nausea and vomiting. In reality, however, he gave them syrup of ipecac—a drug that *causes* vomiting.

What happened? The patients' nausea and vomiting disappeared when they took the syrup of ipecac. The women's *belief* in the drug was so potent that it actually counteracted the chemistry of the drug.[12]

One of the most stunning examples of how faith influences even the course of medication is the well-known story of a patient treated by Dr. Bruno Klopfer in the late 1950s. The patient was suffering from widespread lymphoma—a serious cancer of the immune system—that was in its late stages. About that time, a drug called Krebiozen was being touted as a cure for cancer. The patient demanded the drug, and the doctor agreed.

Within two days of taking the drug, the patient had a remarkable turnaround. As one account described it, the large tumors that covered his body began "melting like snowballs." After ten days of treatment with Krebiozen, the patient was released from the hospital, apparently free of cancer. The doctor called it a medical miracle.

A miracle *had* occurred—but it was a miracle of faith. Sadly, that faith was short-lived. A few months after the patient was released from the hospital, newspapers around the country announced that Krebiozen was worthless. The patient's tumors promptly returned.

Klopfer was fascinated. It was obvious that the patient's faith had healed him once—and Klopfer was convinced it could happen again. He called the patient in, reassured him that the newspaper accounts were inaccurate, and told him an extra-strength refined form of the drug had just been released to physicians. The eager patient accepted the drug. But Klopfer didn't have an improved or refined form of the drug. He gave the patient simple distilled water.

With distilled water coursing through his veins, the patient who believed that he had a potent new form of Krebiozen staged another remarkable recovery. Within days, his tumors again disappeared. He was released from the hospital a second time, apparently free of cancer again.

Unfortunately, it didn't last. Three months after his recovery, the patient read a newspaper report published by the American Medical Association. Definitive tests had proven beyond a doubt that Krebiozen was worthless. Top-ranking officials in the American Medical Association proclaimed the drug useless in the fight against cancer. The patient, who had left the hospital three months earlier free of tumors, read the report. His faith was shattered. His tumors ballooned. Two days after he read the newspaper report, he literally lay down and died.

Faith has a powerful impact on the healing process. Researcher Daniel Goleman calls faith "the hidden ingredient" in every traditional system of healing he knows about. Psychiatrist Jerome Frank says faith is the element in modern medicine that brings about recovery. "The physician's main function is to use his medical skills to stimulate the patient's mechanisms of repair," Frank explains.

"Nonmedical healers, whether African witch doctors or religious faith healers in Western countries, intuitively understand this. Their rituals and laying on of hands are designed to release or strengthen the patient's inner healing powers."[13]

Numerous examples show that faith can heal, even when the faith isn't justified. One of the most striking occurrences happened to New York psychologist Lawrence LeShan, who was asked to do a long-distance faith healing for an extremely painful condition that required immediate and intensive therapy. As LeShan tells it:

> I promised to do the healing that night, and the next morning when [the patient] awoke a "miraculous cure" had occurred. The medical specialist was astounded, and offered to send me pre- and post-healing x-rays and to sponsor publication in a scientific journal. It would have been the psychic healing of the century except for one small detail. In the press of overwork, I had forgotten to do the healing![14]

Medically speaking, faith can move mountains. Sometimes its effect is astonishing. But for most, the power of faith is manifest in small, quiet ways, within our own families, and what results is based not only on our needs, but on a loving Father's will for us and on eternal design.

Is the Lord powerful enough to heal any sickness? Absolutely. But will he always exert his healing power? No. With our eternal perspective, we understand that there may be another, greater, purpose. What, then, of the person who exercises tremendous faith but is not healed of disease? Is faith without merit in such a situation?

Never. When faith does not result in physical healing, faith can bring instead emotional or spiritual healing. It can endow us with quiet strength or the power to endure an illness or bear a situation that would otherwise overwhelm us. Faith can help us face the next day, the next week, or the next month with courage and resolve. It can bring peace. In those cases, the miracle may not be a physical healing but a spiritual insight that turns despair to hope.

Without faith, we may be tempted to give up. With faith, we can say as did one who endured a crisis: "The Lord has not lessened the pain, nor do I understand His purpose, but I am not the fragile, defeated soul I was when all this started. I can clearly see His hand, and I know I will make it."[15] As Elder Neal A. Maxwell assured us, "For the faithful, our finest hours are sometimes during or just following our darkest hours."[16]

Our walk through this world is made easier through faith and, beautifully, is what strengthens faith. As President James E. Faust wrote, "In the pain, the agony, and the heroic endeavors of life, we pass through the refiner's fire, and the insignificant and the unimportant in our lives can melt away like dross and make our faith bright, intact, and strong." The refining process, he added, often seems "cruel and hard," but it is what makes the soul "become like soft clay in the hands of the Master."[17] Faith, wrote President George Albert Smith, "is the principle that points us heavenward and gives us hope in the battle of life."[18]

As President Ezra Taft Benson so eloquently described it:

> Faith gives us vision of what may happen, hope for the future, and optimism in our present tasks. . . . We will all have disappointments and discouragements—that is part of life. But if we will have faith, our setbacks will be but a moment and success will come out of our seeming failures. Our Heavenly Father can accomplish miracles through each of us if we will but place our confidence and trust in Him.[19]

END NOTES

1. Bruce R. McConkie, *The Mortal Messiah,* Vol. 3 (Salt Lake City: Deseret Book, 1980), p. 284.
2. James E. Talmage, *Jesus the Christ,* 15th edition, revised (Salt Lake City: The Church of Jesus Christ of Latter-day Saints, 1977), p. 188.
3. Bruce R. McConkie, *The Mortal Messiah,* Vol. 2 (Salt Lake City: Deseret Book, 1980), p. 46.
4. Ibid.

5. Spencer W. Kimball, *Brigham Young University Speeches of the Year* (Provo, Utah: BYU Press, 1963), p. 6.
6. Bruce R. McConkie, *The Mortal Messiah,* Vol. 2 (Salt Lake City: Deseret Book, 1980), pp. 12-13.
7. Ezra Taft Benson, *Conference Report,* October 1986, p. 59.
8. Studies summarized from "Review Confirms 'Healing' Effects," *New Sense Bulletin,* Vol. 16, No. 8, 1991, p. 1.
9. Herbert Benson, *Beyond the Relaxation Response* (New York: Times Books, 1984), pp. 3-4.
10. Ibid., p. 4.
11. Bernie Siegel, *Peace, Love, and Healing* (New York: Harper and Row, 1989), p. 21.
12. Herbert Benson and Eileen M. Stuart, *The Wellness Book* (New York: Birch Lane Press, 1992), p. 9.
13. Jerome D. Frank, "Emotional Reactions of American Soldiers to an Unfamiliar Disease," *American Journal of Psychiatry,* Vol. 102, pp. 631-40.
14. Larry Dossey, *Healing Words* (San Francisco: Harper San Francisco, 1993), p. 78.
15. "How to Cope With Emotional Crisis," *Church News,* November 3, 1985, p. 15.
16. Neal A. Maxwell, *Conference Report,* April 1984, p. 29.
17. James E. Faust, "The Refiner's Fire," *Ensign,* May 1979, p. 53.
18. George Albert Smith, *Sharing the Gospel with Others* (Salt Lake City: Deseret Book, 1948), p. 62.
19. Ezra Taft Benson, "Four Keys for Success," in an address to the Churubusco Mexico Stake, June 5, 1982.

It is Not Good That Man Should Be Alone

Latter-day Saints should actually be concerned more about the quality of their relationships than are others, because we understand that we are going to be together with others, not only the rest of our lives, but everlastingly. Clearly, therefore, ours are not fleeting relationships. . . . We do not know any "mere mortals." This is true of family life, of friendships, of collegial associations at work, in neighborhoods, and in the Church.

— NEAL A. MAXWELL

CHAPTER

5

Social Support, Relationships, and Health

In his Sunday morning address to the October 1996 General Conference, President Gordon B. Hinckley shared a letter he had received from a single woman struggling to rear four boys on her own. Although there was not another parent in the home, she wrote, "I am not alone. I have a wonderful 'ward family' that has rallied around us."[1]

President Hinckley then went on to describe the type of support this woman had received. Her Relief Society president had supported her emotionally through her greatest hardships, encouraging her spiritual growth, personal prayer, and temple attendance. Faithful home teachers had given each of her boys a priesthood blessing at the beginning of the school year.

Her bishop had been generous in providing needed food and clothing, helped send two of the boys to camp, and helped her work out a budget so she could do as much as possible on her own. Her stake president and counselors had taken the time to visit with her often—at church, over the phone, and in her home. Various priesthood leaders, she said, had been instrumental in keeping her boys active in the Church and in the Scouting program. Three of her sons had achieved the rank of Eagle Scout.

Though, as she described it, "life has been hard," she wrote that "we are always met with loving hearts and warm handshakes. The Christ-like attitude of the stake and our ward has helped us through trials we never imagined possible."[2]

Commenting on the letter, President Hinckley said:

> What a great letter that is. How much it says about the way this Church functions and should function throughout the world. I hope that every woman who finds herself in the kind of circumstances in which this woman lives, is similarly blessed with an understanding and helpful bishop, with a Relief Society president who knows how to assist her, with home teachers who know where their duty lies and how to fulfill it, and with a host of ward members who are helpful without being intrusive.[3]

Undoubtedly, the woman President Hinckley spoke of was sustained in a very real way by the food, clothing, and monetary help she received from her bishop. But even more important to her well-being was *social support*—the degree to which her basic social needs were met through interaction with other people. Crucial to her health and happiness were the "loving hearts and warm handshakes," her knowledge that she could count on other people for help with a problem or support in time of crisis. She and her boys, she wrote, are "living proof . . . that a 'ward family' can make all the difference."

Studies have shown that Mormon men and women generally live longer and are healthier than average. Researchers believe their health and longevity is due to many factors—among them the Word of Wisdom, which discourages the use of alcohol, tobacco, tea, coffee, and harmful drugs and encourages the use of whole grains and fresh vegetables; the practice of resting from labors one day a week; and the avoidance of sexual promiscuity.

But even more important than these factors may be the Church's strong emphasis on social support. Members of the

Church are more likely to be married, and more likely to marry only once. They traditionally have large, close-knit families, and they stay in touch with members of their extended families. They participate in a wide range of Church activities, including well-organized groups. There are obvious sources of social support: involved bishoprics and stake presidencies, caring Relief Society presidents, committed youth leaders, faithful home teachers, concerned visiting teachers. Perhaps, then, the home teaching and visiting teaching programs of the Church are important for more than simply "checking" on the well-being of members; these simple visits may in themselves help protect health and life.

Not as immediately obvious but just as important in terms of social support are the frequent opportunities to work and serve others. The Book of Mormon itself gives us the charge to provide social support. Those who want to come into the fold of God, said Alma, "are willing to bear one another's burdens, that they may be light; Yea, and are willing to mourn with those that mourn; yea, and comfort those that stand in need of comfort" (Mosiah 18:8-9). Each calling we receive in the Church, says Elder Henry B. Eyring, "is a sacred responsibility for others,"[4] though we often do not recognize callings as such.

That obligation extends beyond the formality of a Church calling, as President James E. Faust reminded us:

> To remain true and faithful through this mortal veil of tears, we must love God with all our heart, might, mind, and strength and love our neighbors as ourselves. We must also stand together as families; as members of wards and branches, stakes and districts; and as a people. To our neighbors not of our faith we should be as the good Samaritan who cared for the man who fell among thieves. We must gather strength from each other.[5]

Elder Neal A. Maxwell commissioned us as members of the Church that "we, more than others, should carry jumper and tow cables not only in our cars, but also in our hearts, by which means we can send the needed boost or charge of encouragement or the added momentum to mortal neighbors."[6]

By so doing, we protect our own health and the health of those around us. Researchers who conducted a nine-year study of more than seven thousand California residents were able to identify a single factor that most often led to good health and long life: the amount of social support a person enjoys. They concluded that people with social ties—regardless of their source—lived longer than people who were isolated. And people "who have a close-knit network of intimate personal ties with other people seem to be able to avoid disease, maintain higher levels of health, and in general, to deal more successfully with life's difficulties."[7]

The people with many social contacts—a spouse, a close-knit family, a network of friends, church, or other affiliations—lived longer and had better health. People who were socially isolated had poorer health and died earlier. In fact, those who had few ties with other people died at rates two to five times higher than those with good social ties.[8]

"Some well-loved people fall ill and die prematurely," researchers concluded; "some isolates live long and healthy lives. But these occurrences are infrequent. For the most part, people tied closely to others are better able to stay well."[9] As Elder Neal A. Maxwell put it, the Biblical injunction that "it is not good for man to be alone" was first related to the significance of marriage, but "also is a statement of truth which goes beyond that point of reference."[10] Growing scientific evidence shows that it does, in fact, relate to physical well-being.

As mentioned, social support is the degree to which our basic social needs are met through interaction with other people. It is the perception that we can count on other people for help in a crisis. Leading researchers say it involves five components:[11]

- Being cared for and loved, with the opportunity for shared intimacy
- Being esteemed and valued; having a sense of personal worth

- Sharing companionship, communication, and mutual obligations with others; having a sense of belonging
- Having access to information, appraisal, advice, and guidance from others
- Having access to physical or material assistance

The resources our social network provide may come in the form of tangible aid—lending us money, driving us to a doctor's appointment, doing our grocery shopping, or caring for our children when we are ill. But another kind of resource is equally important: it's the emotional, "intangible" kind of help, such as affection, understanding, acceptance, and esteem.[12]

Social support can come from family members, friends, members of our ward or branch, neighbors, professional associates, people who belong to the same bowling league, and so on. The people who make up our social network are the people with whom we associate, the ones we can turn to in time of need. Where we get our greatest social support depends in part on our gender, age, and other factors.

Interestingly, the richness of our social support depends on what we put into it as much as what we take from it. A study of 700 elderly adults showed that their health and vitality had more to do with what they *contributed* to their social support network than what they *received* from it.[13] Jesus gave us an awesome injunction with the charge to "feed my sheep" (John 21:16); perhaps his bid has as much or more to do with the emotional and spiritual nourishment we give than our random offerings of tangible aid.

Our perspective on our origins brings into sharp focus the admonition contained in the second commandment: "Thou shalt love thy neighbor as thyself" (Mark 12:31). Elder Neal A. Maxwell asks, "How can one really love and serve his neighbor if he ignores the divinely designed purposes of the universe? How can we fully serve our neighbor if we do not acknowledge who our neighbor really is?"[14] In summing up years of research, University of Maryland psychosomatic medicine specialist Dr. James Lynch remarked, "The mandate to 'Love your neighbor as you love yourself' is not just a moral mandate. It's a physiological mandate. Caring is biological. One thing you get from caring for others is you're not lonely; and the more connected you are to life, the healthier you are."[15]

No one knows for sure how social support works to protect health, but it is a proven factor in research that spans five decades. One long-term study of almost three thousand adults in Tecumseh, Michigan, started when each adult was given a thorough physical exam to rule out any existing illness that would force a person to become isolated. Researchers then watched the people closely for the next ten years, making special note of their social relationships and group activities. Those who were socially involved had the best health. When social ties were interrupted or broken, disease increased significantly. Based on their work, the researchers decided that interrupted social ties actually seemed to suppress the body's immune system.[16] The researchers called close personal relationships a "safety net" that helps protect against a variety of diseases.

We seem to derive an odd sort of comfort from other people, a comfort that can literally influence us biologically. And that comfort begins early in life. Psychologist Joan Borysenko describes the effect of social support on infants:

> The consequences of emotional abandonment are no less serious than those of physical abandonment. Babies in foundling homes that are fed and changed on schedule but starved emotionally often develop a syndrome called hospitalism or failure to thrive. No one is present to coo when the baby coos, to smile when the baby smiles, to mirror back its existence to the child. As a result of this loneliness, the babies' pituitary glands fail to produce sufficient growth hormone and the children wither away despite adequate nutrition. Many of these children die before reaching toddlerhood, and those who do survive are often severely damaged psychologically.[17]

The effects of loneliness and isolation continue throughout life. One of the most dramatic examples occurs when people relocate:

those who are uprooted and forced to move away from familiar people and places often get sick. Researchers were able to gauge the effect of disruption by watching coal miners and their families who were moved from small valleys in Appalachia to the company towns created when the coal mines were reopened. By looking at the family names of the miners, it was possible to determine how many had relatives living in the towns to which they had come. Those who moved to towns where they had no relatives had a significantly higher rate of absenteeism due to sickness. The coal miners who moved near relatives stayed significantly healthier. The only real factor that distinguished the two groups was the amount of social support they had.[18]

A fascinating study conducted on the Sinai peninsula gives particular insight into relocation, disrupted ties, friendships, and the presence of kinfolk.[19] In 1972, an Israeli community named Ophira was established at the southernmost tip of the Sinai peninsula, inhabited primarily by families with a pioneering spirit who wanted to build a town in the desert. Geographically, Ophira was isolated; the closest town of any size was more than two hundred miles away.

Because of its geographic isolation, Ophira quickly became self-contained and self-sufficient, both physically and psychologically. Not only were the residents of the town self-sufficient, but they were unusually similar to each other, partly because the living conditions in the community were so uniform. All the people in town lived in a single housing complex. There was only one shopping center, one school, and one medical center with one doctor and one nurse, so everyone in town also shared the same support services.

Ten years after it was established, Ophira was disbanded as part of the Camp David accords with Egypt, which ordered evacuation of the Sinai peninsula. The residents of Ophira, who had lived as such a tightly knit group for ten years, were forced to evacuate and were relocated over a widely scattered area throughout Israel. Some residents were relocated to rural areas, and others moved to urban areas.

Researchers assessed the residents six weeks before the final evacuation, and again two years later. They concentrated on husband–wife pairs who were similar in age, ethnic background, educational level, and occupational status. They reported several interesting findings:

- The demoralization and distress that stem from stressful life events (such as relocation) is long-lasting, not temporary. Tests showed that the stress of relocation was basically as severe after two years as it was six weeks before the actual evacuation.
- The size of a person's social network remains remarkably stable. Each person in the study was asked to list his or her friends six weeks before the evacuation, and again two years later. As could be predicted, the first list of friends consisted almost entirely of other Ophira residents. The list made two years later contained an entirely new group of friends, with only one or two Ophira residents still included. But in almost all cases, the *size* of the lists was almost exactly the same at two years as they had been at six weeks! Even though the friends themselves had changed, the size of the network remained about the same. The size of a person's network, then, depends not on environment and circumstances, but on personal effort.
- A strong social relationship with relatives protects health even more than a strong relationship with friends. Few of the couples in the study had kinfolk in Ophira, and few moved to areas where their kinfolk were. But those who had strong ties with their kinfolk tended to maintain them and draw strength from them, regardless of where they lived. Unlike friends, family members seem to be a source of strength even at distances.

Another study of relocation involved children in World War II England who were separated from their parents and relocated to safer areas.[20] The children in both situations were under a tremendous amount of stress; those who remained with their parents lived with the constant stress of physical danger from the war. The children who had been moved to safer areas to escape the danger of physical injury suffered the stress of being separated from their parents.

Which group fared best? The children who stayed with their parents showed the fewest signs of stress, even though they lived with the daily threat of injury from the enemy blitz. The children who showed the worst signs of stress were those who had lost their primary source of social support—their parents—even though they were physically safer.

California psychiatrist Robert Taylor summed up the protective nature of social ties: "When people have close relationships, they feel less threatened, less alone, more confident, and more in control. Knowing you have people you can turn to in times of need can provide some very important feelings of security, optimism, and hope—all of which can be great antidotes to stress."[21]

According to research, social support can protect even against the most disruptive kinds of stresses, such as unemployment. Researchers studied 110 men who lost their jobs when a plant closed. The men were given thorough exams both before and after the plant closed; examiners measured cholesterol levels, symptoms of illness, symptoms of depression, and the amount of social support each man had from family and friends.

The result showed the importance of social support. The men who had little social support were significantly more likely to get sick, become depressed, and suffer from high cholesterol levels. Those with good support from family and friends were significantly more healthy, despite the stress of losing their jobs.[22]

Epidemiologist Leonard Syme says social support is critical in helping people deal with "battle stress"—not the kind encountered in combat, but the kind real people contend with every day. He remarked that "people who have a close-knit network of intimate personal ties with other people seem to be able to avoid disease, maintain higher levels of health, and in general, to deal more successfully with life's difficulties."[23]

One widely acclaimed study demonstrates exactly how important social support is to people who deal with "battle stress" in their lives. Called "The Tenderloin Senior Outreach Project,"[24] it was a ten-year study that delved into San Francisco's seedy

Tenderloin District—a cluster of low-priced, single-room-occupancy hotels crammed with the poverty-stricken elderly. The district was characterized by skyrocketing crime rates, deteriorating housing conditions, poor access to food, and remarkably bad physical and mental health among its residents.

A group of researchers from the University of California at Berkeley School of Public Health organized weekly support groups for the elderly residents of the district. Then they organized "Safehouse Project," in which more than eighty stores and agencies in the neighborhood became places of refuge where residents could flee in case of emergency. The students from Berkeley acted as leaders in organizing groups of hotel residents, but, buoyed by each other's strength, the residents themselves soon began working on their problems.

The results were dramatic. Several resident groups formed "minimarkets" in the lobbies of their hotels so that residents could get fresh fruits and vegetables. Other groups successfully blocked attempts to increase rents. Still others were able to get food services restored to several of the hotels. And still others succeeded in getting the city to enhance public transportation access to the district.

In the eighteen months following the project's start, crime dropped by a startling 26 percent. The nutritional status of hotel residents improved dramatically. So did their physical and mental health. Researchers delighted in the example of one elderly resident, who had habitually checked himself in to mental institutions every month or so for "reality orientation." After two years of involvement with the program, his monthly visits stopped completely. When researchers asked him about it, he quipped, "I'm a co-leader of my hotel support group, a founder of the anticrime project, and a member of the Mayor's Task Force on Aging. I don't have time for reality!"[25]

Research has shown that social support has a very specific impact on the body, especially on the heart, as demonstrated by a landmark study in Roseto, Pennsylvania, a close-knit Italian-American community nestled among other traditional eastern communities. Residents there were typical of Americans when it came to exercise, cigarette smoking, obesity, high blood pressure, and stress; their diets were higher in fat, cholesterol, and red meat than the average American diet. But the men in Roseto had only about one-sixth the heart disease and deaths from heart disease as random groups in the United States. The rates for Roseto's women were even better.

Researchers concluded that a strong sense of community and strong social ties were what protected the people in Roseto. Stewart Wolf, professor at Temple University School of Medicine and one of the study's researchers, pointed out that

> more than any other town we studied, Roseto's social structure reflected old-world values and traditions. There was a remarkable cohesiveness and sense of unconditional support within the community. Family ties were very strong. And what impressed us most was the attitude toward the elderly. In Roseto, the older residents weren't put on a shelf; they were promoted to "supreme court." No one was ever abandoned.[26]

Then things started to change in Roseto. Younger generations started moving away, marrying "outsiders," severing the close emotional ties to the "old neighborhood." And when that happened, the physical health of the Rosetans began to deteriorate. By the mid-1970s, the heart disease and death rates of people in Roseto were comparable to surrounding Pennsylvania communities. Simply stated, when the social ties started to vanish, so did the protection. "The most important factors in health are the intangibles—things like trust, honesty, loyalty, team spirit. In terms of preventing heart disease, it's just possible that morale is more important than jogging or not eating butter," said the researchers.

Other research also shows that strong social support can help reduce the risk factors for heart disease. One well-known risk factor for heart disease is the Type A personality—the hard-driving, competitive, stressed, and hostile individual. Researchers at Duke Medical Center wanted to find out what factors might help modify the risk to Type A patients, so they interviewed 113 patients who had come to the hospital for x-rays to diagnose how much coronary blockage was in the arteries of the heart.

They found that the Type A personalities who had strong social support were on a par with Type B personalities—the much more relaxed, easy-going person who is much less prone to heart disease. The Type A personalities who were isolated or who had weak social support had the most severe heart disease. The researchers concluded that social support modifies the long-term health consequences of the Type A behavior pattern.[27]

Perhaps one reason that social support protects health is that it appears to improve immune function. Many studies show that strong interpersonal relationships protect the functioning of the immune system, even in the face of stress.[28] Ohio State University psychologist Janice Kiecolt-Glaser found that people who were the loneliest—who had the lowest levels of social support—had immune systems that didn't function as well as those with good social support. In particular, they had lower levels of natural killer cells, an important part of the immune system that helps fight viruses and cancerous tumors.[29]

Because of its impact on the immune system, social support may help determine the outcome of cancer. In a landmark study done at Stanford University Medical School, researchers divided breast cancer patients into two groups. The first group received traditional medical treatment. The second group received weekly group therapy sessions in addition to traditional medical treatment; on the average, they lived twice as long following diagnosis as the women in the first group. The only difference between the women in the two groups was social support.[30] In a similar study at UCLA involving patients with malignant melanoma, the patients in the support group had 60 percent fewer deaths and approximately half as many recurrences of melanoma as the patients who were not in the support groups.[31]

Larry Dossey, co-chair of the newly established Panel on Mind/Body Interventions at the National Institutes of Health, describes the power of social support this way:

> The power of love to change bodies is legendary, built into folklore, common sense, and everyday experience. Love moves the flesh, it pushes matter around—as the blushing and palpitations experienced by lovers attest. Throughout history, "tender loving care" has uniformly been recognized as a valuable element in healing.[32]

Being surrounded by even a few good people who love us, who can act as friends and confidants, not only brings better health, but can prolong our lives as well. Healthy people with good social support are at consistently lower risk for death than are people who are isolated.[33] Socially isolated people—the unmarried, divorced, widowed, people with few friends, and people who have few church or social contacts—are three times as likely to die of a wide variety of diseases than those who live happy, fulfilling social lives.[34]

Social support is such a powerful factor that it even lowers death rates among people who are unhealthy, such as heart attack survivors. One group of researchers concluded that "it appears that being married or unmarried, living with someone or living alone, are not as critical to surviving a heart attack as just having *someone* to turn to for emotional support. And this support seems to work like a drug—the higher the dose, the greater the protective effect."[35]

In a California study of more than seven thousand people over a nine-year period, the people with the most social contacts had the lowest mortality rates; those with the fewest social contacts had the highest rates.[36] And in the ten-year Michigan study discussed earlier in this chapter, the people who were most socially isolated died at *four times* the rate of those who were more socially involved.[37]

Some of the most fascinating evidence regarding social ties and long life came from studies of Japanese people. People in Japan—even though they are more likely to smoke cigarettes, have high blood pressure, endure crushing stress, and live in polluted and crowded cities—enjoy the longest life expectancy in the world. Researchers decided that the Japanese are protected from ill health and death by their unusually close ties to friends, family members, and community. Their strong social support protects them.

As Latter-day Saints, not one among us should feel estranged. According to Elder James M. Paramore, we share the love of God when we reach out to others, and men and women "touched and changed by this love of God begin to look upon their neighbors with profound respect and awe for who they are, what their potential really is as children of an eternal father. . . . Man's spirit reaches out to everyone, for now there is no enmity, no envy, no restricting philosophies, pride, or vanity—even language does not separate men—there is only an openness and oneness with the Spirit and the will of God."[38]

That charge applies especially to our responsibility for drawing in those who are new around us. Referring to those who have recently joined the Church, Elder Neal A. Maxwell challenges us:

> When all these individuals have come from so great a distance, surely we can go a second mile in friendshipping and fellowshipping them! If with quiet heroism they can make their way across the border into belief, surely we can cross a crowded foyer to extend the hand of fellowship. Has it been so long that we have forgotten our first anxious day at a new school or our timidity in a new neighborhood? In the city of Zion, there are constantly new kids on the block![39]

If you need to strengthen your own social connectedness, try some of these suggestions:

- Make your needs known; let others know you're interested in strengthening your friendships and your circle of support.
- Look for groups to join in the community, at church, or at work. Find a group that you feel comfortable in and that deals with a subject you're interested in learning more about.
- Consider enrolling in special classes (such as how to create furniture from willows), special courses (such as how to administer cardiopulmonary resuscitation), or adult education classes offered through your local school district. These classes are widely varied in subject; almost everyone can find something of real interest.

- Find a cause you're committed to, and volunteer.
- Plan now for what you'll be doing a year from now, ten years from now, and during your retirement. Too many people restrict their social connections to the workplace; once they retire, they become isolated and lonely. Make active decisions now to help you stay involved.

We, more than any other people, should seek fulfilling relationships, because we know they will endure beyond this mortal sphere. With death, taught President Spencer W. Kimball, comes "a change of condition into a wider, serener sphere of action; it means the beginning of eternal life, a never-ending existence. It means the continuation of family life, the reuniting of family groups, the perpetuation of friendships, relationships, and associations."[40]

President Joseph F. Smith made the doctrine clear when he wrote, "We are living for eternity and not merely for the moment. Death does not part us from one another. . . . Our relationships are formed for eternity."[41]

The eternal nature of relationships pertains not only to the family, but to the other relationships in our lives. As Elder Neal A. Maxwell wrote, "You and I are believers in and preachers of a glorious gospel that can deepen all human relationships now as well as projecting all relationships into eternity. Friendships, as well as families, are forever."[42] On another occasion he wrote, "The gospel of Jesus Christ is anything but monastic. We are here to light the world, to leaven mankind, and this can only be done by some shared enterprises in the spirit of fellowship and of friendship."[43]

As an example, we have the Savior—the One who is an example in all things. His beckoning friendship is actually an invitation, in which he pleads with us, "I will call you friends, for ye are my friends, and ye shall have an inheritance with me" (D&C 93:45).

END NOTES

1. Gordon B. Hinckley, "Women of the Church," *Conference Report,* October 1996, p. 68.

2. Ibid., p. 69.
3. Ibid.
4. Henry B. Eyring, "Witnesses for God," *Ensign,* November 1996, p. 31.
5. James E. Faust, "Woman Why Weepest Thou?" *Ensign,* November 1996, p. 53.
6. Neal A. Maxwell, *All These Things Shall Give Thee Experience* (Salt Lake City: Deseret Book, 1980), p. 56.
7. Emrika Padus, *The Complete Guide to Your Emotions and Your Health* (Emmaus, Penn.: Rodale Press, 1986), pp. 83-84.
8. Meredith Minkler, "The Social Component of Health," *American Journal of Health Promotion,* Fall 1986, pp. 33-38.
9. Marc Pilisuk and Susan Hillier Parks, *The Healing Web* (Hanover, N.H.: The University Press of New England, 1986), p. 30.
10. Neal A. Maxwell, *For the Power Is in Them: Mormon Musings* (Salt Lake City: Deseret Book, 1970), p. 54.
11. Terrence L. Amick and Judith K. Ockene, "The Role of Social Support in the Modification of Risk Factors for Cardiovascular Disease," in Sally A. Shumaker and Susan M. Czajkowski, *Social Support and Cardiovascular Disease* (New York: Plenum Press, 1994), pp. 260-61.
12. Deborah Preston and Jorge Grimes, "A Study of Differences in Social Support," *Journal of Gerontological Nursing,* Vol. 13, No. 2, pp. 36-40.
13. C. E. Depner and B. Ingersoll-Dayton, "Supportive Relationships in Later Life," *Psychology and Aging,* Vol. E, No. 4, 1988, pp. 348-357.
14. Neal A. Maxwell, *Notwithstanding My Weakness* (Salt Lake City: Deseret Book, 1981), pp. 25-26.
15. Brent Q. Hafen and Kathryn J. Frandsen, *People Who Need People Are the Healthiest People: The Importance of Relationships* (Evergreen, Colo.: Cordillera Press, 1987).
16. Ibid.
17. Joan Borysenko, *Fire in the Soul* (New York: Warner Books, 1993), p. 83.
18. Marc Pilisuk and Susan Hillier Parks, *The Healing Web* (Hanover, N.H.: The University Press of New England, 1986), p. 32.
19. From Peter Steinglass, Eli Weisstraub, and Atara Kaplan De-Nour, "Perceived Personal Networks as Mediators of Stress Reactions," *American Journal of Psychiatry,* Vol. 145, No. 10, 1988, pp. 1259-63.

20. Blair Justice, *Who Gets Sick: Thinking and Health* (Houston, Tex.: Peak Press, 1987), p. 128.
21. Brent Q. Hafen and Kathryn J. Frandsen, *People Who Need People Are the Healthiest People: The Importance of Relationships* (Evergreen, Colo.: Cordillera Press, 1987).
22. Meredith Minkler, "The Social Component of Health," *American Journal of Health Promotion,* Fall 1986, pp. 33-38.
23. Emrika Padus, *The Complete Guide to Your Emotions and Your Health* (Emmaus, Penn.: Rodale Press, 1986), p. 472.
24. Robert Ornstein and David Sobel, *The Healing Brain: A Scientific Reader* (New York: Simon and Schuster, 1987), pp. 197-99.
25. Brent Q. Hafen and Kathryn J. Frandsen, *People Who Need People Are the Healthiest People: The Importance of Relationships* (Evergreen, Colo.: Cordillera Press, 1987).
26. Ibid.
27. "Friendship: Heart Saver for Type A's," *Men's Health,* November 1987, p. 4.
28. S. Kennedy, J. Kiecolt-Glaser, and R. Glaser, "Immunological Consequences of Acute and Chronic Stressors: Mediating Role of Interpersonal Relationships," *British Journal of Medical Psychology,* Vol. 61, 1988, pp. 77-85.
29. Editors of *Prevention* magazine and the Center for Positive Living, *Positive Living and Health: The Complete Guide to Brain/Body Healing and Mental Empowerment* (Emmaus, Penn.: Rodale Press, 1990), p. 231.
30. David Spiegel, "A Psychological Intervention and Survival Time of Patients with Metastatic Breast Cancer," *Advances,* Vol. 7, No. 3, 1991, pp. 10-19.
31. Fawzy I. Fawzy, "Malignant Melanoma: Effects of an Early Structured Psychiatric Intervention, Coping, and Affective State of Recurrence and Survival Six Years Later," *Archives of General Psychiatry,* Vol. 50, 1993, pp. 681-89.
32. Larry Dossey, *Healing Words* (San Francisco: Harper San Francisco, 1993), p. 109.
33. Sheldon Cohen, "Social Support and Physical Illness," in *Advances,* Vol. 7, No. 1, 1990, pp. 35-48.
34. Jeff Meade, "How to Enrich Your Relationships," *Prevention,* March 1988, pp. 86-89.
35. "Surviving a Heart Attack: Emotional Support is Key," *Mental Medicine Update,* Spring 1993, p. 2.

36. Emrika Padus, *The Complete Guide to Your Emotions and Your Health* (Emmaus, Penn.: Rodale Press, 1986), p. 83.
37. Steven Locke and Douglas Colligan, *The Healer Within* (New York: E.P. Dutton, 1986), p. 89.
38. James M. Paramore, *Conference Report,* April 1981, p. 75.
39. Neal A. Maxwell, *Conference Report,* October 1980, pp. 16-17.
40. Spencer W. Kimball, *The Teachings of Spencer W. Kimball,* comp. by Edward L. Kimball (Salt Lake City: Bookcraft, 1982), p. 39.
41. Joseph F. Smith, *Gospel Doctrine,* comp. by John A. Widtsoe (Salt Lake City: Deseret Book, 1919), p. 277.
42. Neal A. Maxwell, *All These Things Shall Give Thee Experience* (Salt Lake City: Deseret Book, 1980), p. 56.
43. Neal A. Maxwell, *Deposition of a Disciple* (Salt Lake City: Deseret Book, 1976), p. 38.

The mandate to "Love your neighbor as you love yourself" is not just a moral mandate. It's a physiological mandate. One thing you get from caring for others is you're not lonely; and the more connected you are to life, the healthier you are.

— Dr. James Lynch

Our Father in Heaven, who loves his children, desires for them that which will bring them happiness now and in the eternities to come, and there is no greater happiness than is found in the most meaningful of all human relationships—the companionships of husband and wife and parents and children.

— GORDON B. HINCKLEY

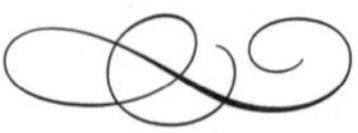

CHAPTER

6

Marriage, Families, and Health

As articulated by President Gordon B. Hinckley, one of the features that sets the Church apart from other modern-day sects is "a belief in the divine nature of the family as an institution ordained of God. Here center the most sacred of all human relationships," he explains. "Life is eternal. Love is eternal. And God our Eternal Father designed and has made it possible that our families shall be eternal."[1]

We get some glimpse of the importance of the family from Lehi, who fled Jerusalem under divine tutelage. Of all he owned, we are told, Lehi "took nothing with him, save it were his family" (1 Nephi 2:4). The family, taught President Ezra Taft Benson, is a "divine institution established by our Heavenly Father." As such, it is basic to civilization. "The establishment of a home is not only a privilege, but marriage and the bearing, rearing, and proper training of children is a duty of the highest order."[2]

The family, of course, begins with marriage. In the final months before his death, the Prophet Joseph Smith chose to give several last words of instruction to the Church he would soon leave behind. One set of instructions, profound in its brevity, detailed exactly why marriage is of such consequence:

> In the celestial glory, there are three heavens or degrees;
>
> And in order to obtain the highest, a man must enter into this order of the priesthood [meaning the new and everlasting covenant of marriage];
>
> And if he does not, he cannot obtain it.
>
> He may enter into the other, but that is the end of his kingdom; he cannot have an increase. (D&C 131:1-4.)

Honorable marriage, said President Ezra Taft Benson, "is more important than wealth, position, and status. As husband and wife, you can achieve your life's goals together. As you sacrifice for each other and your children, the Lord will bless you, and your commitment to the Lord and your service in his kingdom will be enhanced."[3]

"Marriage, designed to be an eternal covenant, is the most glorious and most exalting principle of the gospel of Jesus Christ," he wrote on another occasion. "Faithfulness to the marriage covenant brings the fullest joy here and glorious rewards hereafter."[4]

President Benson added that such joy was never intended to be buried in the grave. In an address on the family to an audience in Seattle, Washington, he confirmed:

> Did the God of Heaven who created and intended marriage and family to be the source of man's greatest joy, his dearest possession while on this earth, intend that it end at death? Do marriage and families pertain only to this transitory state? Are all our sympathies, affections, and love for each other a thing of naught, to be cast off in death? We testify that Joseph Smith was a prophet raised up by God to restore many great truths which had been lost because of the absence of revelation. Through him God revealed the eternity of the marriage covenant and the timelessness of the family.[5]

A basic tenet of The Church of Jesus Christ of Latter-day Saints, eternal marriage is one of the principles that sets us apart from other contemporary churches. Our perspective of marriage as an eternal partnership gives spiritual strength to what some in the world consider to be easily discarded. But marriage goes beyond boosting spiritual strength: scientific evidence now shows that marriage—a good one, that is—can also help protect people from illness and disease, help them bounce back more quickly when they do get sick, and even help people live longer. If current research is accurate, people who are divorced or unhappily married don't fare nearly as well in terms of health and long life.

Government researchers with the National Center for Health Statistics completed a survey of nearly 123,000 Americans nationwide. They found that married people have fewer health problems than unmarried people. Charlotte Schoenborn, who was instrumental in conducting the study, said the results demonstrate "there is still a clear association between being well and being married," despite recent trends away from marriage in America.

Researchers with the well-respected Framingham Heart Study tracked the health of more than five thousand people for more than three decades. Among their conclusions was a testimony for the health benefits of marriage: they reported that getting—and staying—married was a predictor for a long, healthy life.

Statistics from a multitude of studies show the same thing: happy marriage dramatically increases life expectancy. In fact, a man who marries can expect to automatically add about nine years and seven months to his life.[6] One researcher went so far as to say that some of the increased death rates in unmarried people are "astounding," rising as high as *ten times* the rates for married people of the same ages. The researcher sums up:

> The overall death rate for divorced individuals in the United States is almost double that of married individuals. For every major cause of death, rates for divorced males range anywhere from two to six times higher than those of

> their married counterparts. Single and widowed males show similarly high death rates when compared to those who were married.[7]

Married people live longer because they are not as prone to disease, apparently because marriage keeps the immune system strong. Scientific studies show that immune system function—measured by blood tests—is strongest and best among those who are married. Next are singles (those who have never been married). Singles are followed by those who have been widowed. And the group of people with the lowest immune system function are those who are divorced or separated.

According to the National Health Interview Survey, married people even report fewer injuries per year than single and divorced people but, interestingly, more than widowed people. According to the survey, divorced people have "by far" the highest rate of injuries, with divorced women having more than twice as many as married women.[8]

Divorce, in fact, has been shown to profoundly affect the health of both children and adults who are involved. It may be the longest-lasting for children. Researcher Ann S. Masten points out:

> A stressful event rarely occurs in isolation. Divorce is not a single event, but a series of related events embedded in the ongoing lives of people. It often occurs in the context of extreme family conflict and emotional crisis. It can precipitate recurrent financial problems and separations, custodial conflicts, changes of school, home, and daily routine. Above all, divorce can be so devastating to the parents that the children temporarily lose the most important protective factor in their lives, a healthy, well-functioning caregiver.[9]

For children, divorce is one of the most disruptive events possible, and it leads to changes in biological health. Children almost universally experience divorce as a profound personal, familial, and social loss.[10] In addition to having health problems, most children involved in divorce suffer emotional and behavioral changes that can also impact health. Adding insult to injury, most divorced families end up with less affluence, forcing children, along with the rest of the family, to adjust to a whole new spectrum of reduced economic advantages.

Unfortunately, a high number of children are likely to be involved in divorce. During the past three decades, Americans have virtually remade society—and, along with it, the family. Statistics tell at least part of the story: according to a special issue of *Newsweek*, today's American family is likely to be much different than Ozzie and Harriet or the Cleavers were:

> The divorce rate has doubled since 1965 . . . and demographers project that half of all first marriages made today will end in divorce. Six out of ten second marriages will probably collapse. One-third of all children born in the past decade will probably live in a stepfamily before they are eighteen. One out of every four children today is being raised by a single parent. About 22 percent of children today were born out of wedlock; of those, about a third were born to a teenage mother. One out of every five children lives in poverty; the rate is twice as high among blacks and Hispanics.[11]

Children aren't the only ones who face health risks following divorce. Every major study agrees that divorced people—and others who are separated from their spouses—experience more physical and mental illness than those who are married. Divorced people visit physicians significantly more often than do married or single people.[12] According to research, divorce has an equivalent impact on health to smoking a pack of cigarettes a day.[13]

The reason for health risks with divorce may lie with the immune system: research has shown that divorce can actually compromise the immune system, especially during the first year following divorce. The risk of disease in almost every category soars with divorce, and divorce even affects longevity. (The state of Nevada had the second highest death rate in the United States from all causes during the years it was the divorce center of the country.)[14]

Dr. Robert Seagraves of the University of Chicago Medical School points out:

> It is difficult for happily married people to appreciate the extent of disruption caused by divorce. The individual has lost a social network as well as a spouse. Typically, close friends of married couples are themselves married, and many of these friendships are lost following divorce. The divorced individual reenters the world of dating, feeling rusty in middle age, and facing the same insecurities experienced as a teenager.[15]

But what about people who are unhappily married and stick it out? New evidence shows that unhappily married people may be the worst off in terms of good health and long life. Research from a number of studies shows that unhappily married people have poorer health than their single counterparts—even the ones who are divorced. Simply being married doesn't give you a jump-start on good health; being *happily* married does.[16]

One reason for this is that actual physical changes occur during marital conflict. According to researchers at Stanford University, blood pressure skyrockets during marital disputes. Similar research at the University of Washington and the University of California at Berkeley shows that marital conflict affects the heart rate, pulse, and ability of the skin to resist electricity. And new studies show that marital fights actually weaken the immune system, especially in women. When couples in a laboratory were asked to role-play various situations involving dispute, researchers emphasized that "there was a far stronger effect on the immune system than we ever anticipated."[17]

Even with our testimony of the importance of marriage, we know that marriage can be challenging. Sometimes in marriage it helps, says Elder Neal A. Maxwell, "to look back at our climb to see how far we have come."[18] What we bring to the marriage, both at its beginning and throughout our association, can determine our happiness. "A relationship between husband and wife that is characterized by a generosity of spirit and by selflessness can overcome anything that is placed in its path," Elder Maxwell wrote.[19]

In a message written for the youth of the Church but applicable to all, President Ezra Taft Benson said, "The family has serious problems. Divorce is epidemic. The incidence of delinquency is on the rise. The answer is not more marriage counselors or social workers. The answer lies in a husband and wife taking their marriage covenant seriously, realizing that they both have a responsibility to make the marriage a happy one."[20]

President Spencer W. Kimball shared the formula for a happy marriage:

> If two people love the Lord more than their own lives and then love each other more than their own lives, working together in total harmony with the gospel program as their basic structure, they are sure to have this great happiness. When a husband and wife go together frequently to the holy temple, kneel in prayer together in their home with their family, go hand in hand to their religious meetings, keep their lives wholly chaste, mentally and physically, so that their whole thoughts and desires and love are all centered in one being, their companion, and both are working together for the upbuilding of the kingdom of God, then happiness is at its pinnacle.[21]

That view differs dramatically from the view of the world. Both marriage and the family are under attack by the trends in today's world. We are emphasizing marriage and family "in an age when the modern family appears to be disintegrating, when homes are becoming 'hollow hotels,' and when relationships with family and kinsmen are seen as burdens to be jettisoned as soon as possible,"[22] wrote Elder Neal A. Maxwell. President Gordon B. Hinckley decried those trends by proclaiming:

> Fathers and mothers are needed who will rise and stand upon their feet to make of their homes sanctuaries in which children will grow in a spirit of obedience, industry, and fidelity to tested standards of conduct. If our society is coming apart at the seams, it is because the tailor and the seamstress in the home are not producing the kind of stitching that will hold under stress. In the name of giving advantages, we have too often bartered away the real opportunities of our children.[23]

In contrast, the Church teaches us to esteem the family. As Elder John A. Widtsoe wrote:

> In the long eternities we shall not be lonely wanderers, but side by side, with our loved ones who have gone before and those who shall follow, we shall travel the endless journey. What mother does not value this promise! What father does not feel his heart warm towards the eternal possession of his family! . . . Temple marriage becomes a promise of unending joy.[24]

Not only does the family bring spiritual rewards, but it has a strong influence on the health of all members of the family. We know from scientific research that members of weak, stressed families have characteristic health problems; members of strong, healthy families most often enjoy good health; and parents have a tremendous influence on the health and development of children in the family.

A series of observations by Dr. Harry F. Harlow at the University of Wisconsin showed the importance of a parent's presence and touch. It started almost by accident: Harlow noticed that baby monkeys who had cloth pads on the floor of their wire cages were stronger and huskier than the monkeys that had no cloth pad. Interestingly, the babies treated the cloth pad much as a child treats a teddy bear: they cuddled it, caressed it, and played with it.

After watching the baby monkeys with their cloth pads, Harlow was prompted to build a kind of surrogate "mother" for the babies. He built a wire monkey and covered it with soft terrycloth. He outfitted it with a rubber nipple that dispensed milk and placed a light bulb inside it to radiate warmth. The baby monkeys enthusiastically accepted the surrogate.

The enthusiasm of the babies led Harlow to wonder whether the monkeys really needed a "mother" that was so warm and touchable. So he built a second "mother," this one out of wire alone. The wire mother had a nipple that dispensed milk, but no light bulb or soft cloth covering. Four of the baby monkeys were allowed to nurse from the terrycloth mother, while the other four were allowed to nurse only from the wire mother.

Harlow was amazed. All eight monkeys spent most of their time cuddling the terrycloth mother. At feeding time, four went to the wire mother for their milk, but immediately returned to the cloth mother as soon as they were finished eating. Whenever they were frightened, all eight monkeys climbed onto the terrycloth mother for solace.

In other experiments, monkeys were placed in cages with nothing but a wire mother. They took nourishment from her, but many did not survive. Those who did had poor coping skills. When placed under stress, they cowered in a corner, hid their faces under their arms, or screamed. This happened even though they could see, hear, and smell other baby monkeys.

The strong influence of nurturing on early development seems to apply to humans as well. Twenty-five years ago, Dr. Rene Spitz first described *marasmus,* the physical wasting away of infants who suddenly lost their mothers. Some infants who suddenly lost their mothers refused to eat and, even when force-fed, eventually died.[25]

An important factor appears to be loving attention. A British nutritionist in occupied Germany shortly after World War II was puzzled by her observation that children in two orphanages were growing at astoundingly different rates, even though they were fed exactly the same rations. She found that the orphanage where the children were doing well was supervised by a kind matron who had the love and admiration of the children. The orphanage where the children were doing poorly was supervised by a strict disciplinarian who showed little affection for the children in her care.

What happened next was a strong testimony to the importance of closeness and affection. The kind matron left her post to accept other employment and was replaced by the strict disciplinarian. Within a short time, the children who had been thriving started to fall behind and lose weight, even though their diet had been supplemented with bread, jam, and orange juice.

Research has proved that a parent's influence is significant from the moment of birth and that the stability and health of the family as a unit has a profound effect on the health of its individual members. Health problems can often be traced to weak or stressed families. Some family stress is a product of the times: we're a country on the move, which means that extended family members are less likely to be nearby; interaction among family members tends to be limited to a few minutes a day; and the trend toward two-career families has reduced the number of full-time homemakers. Then there are the top ten stresses for today's families: money, discipline, insufficient "couple time," lack of shared responsibility in the family, communication, insufficient "me time," guilt about not accomplishing more, poor marital relationships, not enough family play time, and an overscheduled family calendar.[26]

According to researchers, a handful of traits signify distress in a family: physical symptoms (such as nail-biting or bed-wetting), frequent arguments, too much conflict between husband and wife, burnout, lack of communication, "controlled" arguments (in which problems are buried in silence), lack of interaction with each other, an absence of rewarding relationships outside the family, a lack of affection, and infidelity (including a person who has an "affair" with a hobby, work, or other interest instead of investing time and effort in the marriage).

The result of tension and stress in the family is often illness and stress in individual family members. In a study at Harvard University, members of stressed families picked up strep infections much more often—and those infections developed into illness *four times more often*—than among members of non-stressed families.[27] Other studies have shown that unhealthy families increase the risk of specific diseases, including diabetes, asthma, and cancer.

At Jefferson Medical College in Philadelphia, many cancer patients described their parents as "aloof, cold people."[28] Interestingly, when cancer patients were asked about childhood traumas, they tended to gloss over the death of a parent or sibling; some even had to be prodded to remember that a parent had died when they were very young. They tended to bottle up their emotions; the cancer patients described themselves as "emotionally detached" from their parents. In one long-term study, more negative attitudes about the family were found among the cancer patients than among any other group in the study.[29]

Just as weak or stressed families can cause illness, strong families contribute to good health and long life. One reason is social support: if you belong to a strong, healthy family, you've got "an unconditional charter membership in an emotional support group wherever you roam." The strongest social ties we have are our parents, spouse, siblings, and children. In strong families, members can be counted on to provide practical and concrete aid in times of crisis. As one family counselor put it, "The person from a really supportive family doesn't have to go it alone. That person is part of something bigger: a family that cares enough to let him or her know he or she is okay."[30]

A strong family helps buffer the effects of stress, reducing the risk of illness and disease. The American farm crisis provides a powerful example.[31] During the 1970s, farmers faced incredible odds: production costs skyrocketed, but farmers couldn't sell their goods for enough to cover their costs. Many farmers faced staggering debt; some underwent foreclosure. A number of family farms were destroyed. As many as half the farmers in some states were bankrupt; the rest teetered on the edge, not knowing if theirs would be the next farm on the auction block. In one small Iowa community of only eight thousand, three farmers committed suicide within eighteen months.

Farm families faced not only economic distress, but a sense of personal failure. Some farms had been run by families for generations; loss meant embarrassment and disgrace for many extended family members. Some of these farm families suffered tremendously, but many rallied. They didn't get sick. They fought off stress. They were *families.* The strength of the family enabled it to weather the storm.

There are many ways to help boost the health of a family. One is by having family reunions; researchers have actually found that family reunions promote healing and help protect good health. We can develop family traditions or customs that have special meaning for every family member, or volunteer as a family. It is important to involve the entire family from the beginning, and work together as we carry out our plans.

Additionally, we can incorporate what researchers have identified as healthy family traits:[32] open and positive communication, affirmation and support, respect, trust, enjoyment, interaction, leisure time together, shared responsibility, sense of right and wrong, traditions, religious participation, respect for privacy, service both inside and outside the family, and effective problem-solving abilities.

There are other things, too, we can do to strengthen the family. One is to teach our children the gospel at home. The Book of Mormon reminds us of a people who were highly religious on the surface, but after they had offered up worship in public, they "returned to their homes, never speaking of their God again until they had assembled themselves together again to the holy stand, to offer up thanks after their manner" (Alma 31:23). For the Zoramites, it was a fatal flaw. For us, it is just as fatal. As President Gordon B. Hinckley stated, "This simple practice, a return to family worship, spreading across the land and over the earth, would in a generation largely lift the blight that is destroying us."[33]

Another way to strengthen the family is family home evening: like "iron links in a chain," taught President Ezra Taft Benson, holding regular family home evenings "will bind a family together, in love, pride, tradition, strength, and loyalty."[34]

"It is a striking fact that the family home evening is the ideal time to accomplish almost every type of family togetherness," wrote Elder Dallin H. Oaks. "It is the ideal place for the family to pray together, learn together, counsel together, play together, and even work together."[35]

Still another way to strengthen the family is through family prayer. The resurrected Lord taught the Nephites on the American continent to "Pray in your families unto the Father, always in my name" (3 Nephi 18:21). President Thomas S. Monson told of a prominent American judge, who was asked what citizens of the world could do to reduce crime and disrespect for the law. His answer was simple: "I would suggest a return to the old-fashioned practice of family prayer." As President Monson reflected, "As a people, aren't we grateful that family prayer is not an out-of-date practice with us? There is not a more beautiful sight in this world than to see a family praying together."[36] Elder John H. Groberg said, "I know of no single activity that has more potential for unifying our families and bringing more love and divine direction into our homes than consistent, fervent family prayer."[37]

President Gordon B. Hinckley taught:

> I know of nothing that will ease family tensions, that in a subtle way will bring about the respect for parents which leads to obedience, that will affect the spirit of repentance which will largely erase the blight of broken homes than will praying together, confessing weaknesses together before the Lord and invoking the blessings of the Lord upon the home and those who dwell there.[38]

Elder Neal A. Maxwell wrote that "few of us have a greater chance to do lasting good in the world than in the opportunities we have within our own family every day."[39] In an address on the family delivered at general conference, President David O. McKay told us, "No other success can compensate for failure in the home.

The poorest shack in which love prevails over a united family is of greater value to God and future humanity than any other riches. In such a home God can work miracles and will work miracles."[40]

Those miracles extend far beyond our mortal existence, preparing us for the world of immortality that is to follow. Elder Neal A. Maxwell summed up the importance of the family when he wrote:

> Just as a giant solar flare reaching skyward from our sun ends up causing stormy weather on the earth, today's failure—or success—in an obscure family thousands of miles away may touch us later far more than we know. Dr. Dean E. Turner has written wisely: "Family love is the prism through which God's grace shines brightest into the world. For a world in need of more light and love, how precious a prism the family is!"[41]

END NOTES

1. Gordon B. Hinckley, *Conference Report*, April 1967, p. 54.
2. Ezra Taft Benson, *Teachings of Ezra Taft Benson* (Salt Lake City: Bookcraft, 1988), p. 496.
3. Ibid., p. 497.
4. Ibid., pp. 533-34.
5. Ibid., p. 33.
6. Jo Ann Tooley and Lynn Y. Anderson, "Living Is Risky," *U.S. News and World Report,* January 25, 1988, p. 77.
7. James J. Lynch, *The Broken Heart: The Medical Consequences of Loneliness* (New York: Basic Books, Inc., 1977), p. 69.
8. Emily Friedman, "Marriage May Promote Health," *Medical World News,* December 26, 1988, p. 34.
9. Ann S. Masten, "Stress, Coping, and Children's Health," *Pediatric Annals,* Vol. 14, No. 8, 1985, pp. 544-47.
10. Sheldon Cohen and S. Leonard Syme, eds., *Social Support and Health* (London: Academic Press, Inc., 1985), pp. 32-36.
11. Jerrold K. Footlick, "What Happened to the Family?" *Newsweek* (Special Issue), Winter/Spring 1990, p. 16.

12. Barbara R. Sarason, Irwin G. Sarason, and Gregory R. Pierce, *Social Support: An Interactional View* (New York: John Wiley and Sons, 1990), p. 257.
13. H. Morowitz, "Hiding in the Hammond Report," *Hospital Practice,* August 1975, pp. 35-39.
14. Barbara Powell, *Alone, Alive, and Well* (Emmaus, Penn.: Rodale Press, 1985), p. 62.
15. Brent Q. Hafen and Kathryn J. Frandsen, *People Need People: The Importance of Relationships to Health and Wellness* (Evergreen, Colo.: Cordillera Press, Inc., 1987), p. 85.
16. Barbara S. Sarason, Irwin G. Sarason, and Gregory R. Pierce, *Social Support: An Interactional View* (New York: John Wiley and Sons, 1990), p. 258.
17. Linda Murray, "Mad Marriages: Arguing Your Way to Better Health," *Longevity,* October 1993, p. 30.
18. Neal A. Maxwell, *That My Family Should Partake* (Salt Lake City: Deseret Book, 1974), p. 72.
19. Ibid., p. 74.
20. Ezra Taft Benson, "The Ten Commandments," *The New Era,* July 1978, p. 38.
21. Spencer W. Kimball, *Marriage and Divorce* (Salt Lake City: Deseret Book, 1976), p. 24.
22. Neal A. Maxwell, *A More Excellent Way: Essays on Leadership for Latter-day Saints* (Salt Lake City: Deseret Book, 1973), p. 8.
23. Gordon B. Hinckley, *Conference Report,* October 1968, p. 56.
24. John A. Widtsoe, *Evidences and Reconciliations,* comp. by G. Homer Durham, reprinted (Salt Lake City: Bookcraft, 1960), p. 299.
25. James J. Lynch, *The Broken Heart: The Medical Consequences of Loneliness* (New York: Basic Books, Inc., 1977), pp. 69-71.
26. Dolores Curran, *Stress and the Healthy Family* (Minneapolis: Winston Press, 1985).
27. Blair Justice, *Who Gets Sick: Thinking and Health* (Houston, Tex.: Peak Press, 1987), pp. 37-38.
28. Steven Locke and Douglas Colligan, *The Healer Within: The New Medicine of Mind and Body* (New York: E.P. Dutton, 1986), p. 141.
29. Ibid., p. 145.
30. Sharon Faelten, David Diamond, and the editors of *Prevention* maga-

zine, *Take Control of Your Life: A Complete Guide to Stress Relief* (Emmaus, Penn.: Rodale Press, 1988), p. 273.

31. Phillip L. Rice, *Stress and Health: Principles and Practice for Coping and Wellness* (Monterey, Calif.: Brooks/Cole Publishing, 1987), p. 140.

32. Dolores Curran, *Traits of a Healthy Family* (Minneapolis, Minn.: Winston Press, 1983).

33. Gordon B. Hinckley, *Conference Report,* April 1963, p. 129.

34. Ezra Taft Benson, *Conference Report,* October 1982, p. 60.

35. Dallin H. Oaks, "Parental Leadership in the Family," *Ensign,* June 1985, p. 11.

36. Thomas S. Monson, "Heavenly Homes—Forever Families," *Ensign,* June 1986, p. 6.

37. John H. Groberg, *Conference Report,* April 1982, p. 75.

38. Gordon B. Hinckley, *Conference Report,* April 1963, p. 128.

39. Neal A. Maxwell, *That My Family Should Partake* (Salt Lake City: Deseret Book, 1974), p. 7.

40. David O. McKay, *Conference Report,* April 1964, p. 5.

41. Neal A. Maxwell, *That My Family Should Partake* (Salt Lake City: Deseret Book, 1974), p. 13.

In the long eternities we shall not be lonely wanderers, but side by side, with our loved ones who have gone before and those who shall follow, we shall travel the endless journey.

— JOHN A. WIDTSOE

To those who mourn we speak comfort. Know that your Savior is well acquainted with grief. He who notes the sparrow's fall is aware of you and desires to comfort and bless you. Turn to Him and lay your burden at His feet.

— Ezra Taft Benson

CHAPTER

7

Grief, Loneliness, and Health

The Savior has been described both by the prophets who preceded him and by his contemporaries as "a man of sorrows, and acquainted with grief" (Isaiah 53:3). His was a life that uniquely prepared him to, among other things, understand the depth of grief.

President Spencer W. Kimball shared this insight:

> Christ chose to experience mortality's grief. . . . For more than three decades, he lived a life of hazard and jeopardy. From Herod's bloody debacle in the merciless murder of Bethlehem's infants to Herod's and Pilate's merciless giving him to the human wolves, Jesus was in constant danger. . . . Perilously he lived from day to day with a price on his head, the final price paid being thirty pieces of silver. It seemed that not only human enemies would snarl his life but even his friends would desert him and even Satan and his cohorts would hound him ceaselessly. As it had been predicted, he was a "man of sorrows, and acquainted with grief."[1]

Throughout his life Christ was "despised and rejected of men" (Isaiah 53:3); he "was oppressed, and he was afflicted" (Isaiah 53:7). Because of Christ we have hope to overcome our own grief. Our hope began in the shadowed Garden of Gethsemane. As Elder Bruce R. McConkie described it:

> It was there Jesus took upon himself the sins of the world. . . . It was there he suffered beyond human power to endure. It was there he sweat great drops of blood from every pore. It was there his anguish was so great he fain would have let the bitter cup pass. It was there he made the final choice to follow the will of the Father. It was there that an angel from heaven came to strengthen him in his greatest trial. Many have been crucified, and the torment and pain is extreme. But only one, and he the Man who had God as his Father, has bowed beneath the burden of grief and sorrow that lay upon him in that awful night, that night in which he descended below all things as he prepared himself to rise above them all. . . . And there, at this moment, while he prayed in this garden, was to be centered in him the agony and sorrow of the whole world.[2]

The Book of Mormon prophet describes what Jesus bore at that moment: "And he shall go forth, suffering pains and afflictions and temptations of every kind; and this that the world might be fulfilled which saith he will take upon him the pains and the sicknesses of his people.

"And he will take upon him death, that he may loose the bands of death which bind his people" (Alma 7:11-12).

The Psalmist provided his own vision of what the Lord would feel: "Reproach hath broken my heart; and I am full of heaviness: and I looked for some to take pity, but there was none; and for comforters, but I found none. They gave me also gall for my meat; and in my thirst they gave me vinegar to drink" (Psalm 69:20, 21). Nailed to the cross, Jesus died of what Elder James E. Talmage believes was, literally, "a broken heart."[3] In his sacrifice, he suffered "the pains of all men, yea, the pains of every living creature, both men, women, and children" (2 Nephi 9:21).

Gospel scholar Hugh Nibley describes the result:

> In his darkest hour the Lord told the Apostles, "These things I have spoken unto you, that in me ye might have peace. In the world ye shall have tribulation; but be of good cheer; I have overcome the world" (John 16:33). Then he left them to tread the winepress alone, to do the work that no one else could do. We are commanded to be joyful because he has borne our sorrows. He was a man of sorrows and acquainted with grief so that we need not be. . . . If we remain gloomy after what he did for us, it is because we do not accept what he did for us.[4]

"Born of Mary, rejected by his own, a man of sorrows and acquainted with grief, he bowed beneath an infinite burden in Gethsemane, sweating great drops of blood from every pore," wrote Elder Bruce R. McConkie. "He was crucified. He ministered among the righteous in the world of spirits, and on the third day he burst the bands of death, arising from the Arimathean's tomb in glorious immortality as the firstfruits of them that slept. And in some way, incomprehensible to us but glorious and wondrous to contemplate, the effects of his resurrection pass upon all men so that all shall rise from death to life."[5]

Through the Savior we ourselves can overcome grief. With this assurance, we exclaim with Paul:

> But now is Christ risen from the dead, and become the firstfruits of them that slept. . . .
>
> For as in Adam all die, even so in Christ shall all be made alive. . . .
>
> Behold, I shew you a mystery; We shall not all sleep, but we shall all be changed,
>
> In a moment, in the twinkling of an eye, at the last trump: for the trumpet shall sound, and the dead shall be raised incorruptible, and we shall be changed.

> For this corruptible must put on incorruption, and this mortal must put on immortality.
>
> So when this corruptible shall have put on incorruption, and this mortal shall have put on immortality, then shall be brought to pass the saying that is written, Death is swallowed up in victory.
>
> O, death, where is thy sting? O grave, where is thy victory? . . .
>
> But thanks be to God, which giveth us the victory through our Lord Jesus Christ. (1 Corinthians 15:20, 23, 51-57.)

Each of us will lose people we love to death; that is part of the plan. No one escapes the loss of loved ones and the sorrow that inevitably follows. An old Far Eastern legend tells of a woman who, deep in sorrow over the death of her only son, sought counsel from a holy man. His instructions were simple: he told the woman to travel through the land and gather a flower from the dooryard of each home where there had been no sorrow. She was then to fashion the flowers into a garland, and bring the garland to him. After many days, the woman returned empty-handed. Despite her extensive travels, she had been unable to find a single home whose inhabitants had not been touched by grief.

We need not go door-to-door in our quest for flowers. If we hope to ease our sorrow, we need go no farther than the Savior. The resurrection of Christ and his triumph over death is the key to easing grief and bereavement in this life. "How bitter must be the suffering and grief of those who see nothing beyond the grave except the beginning of eternal night and oblivion," wrote President Heber J. Grant. "For them that thus believe, death has its sting and the grave its victory. To them, even the glory of this earth is but the last flickering of a candle in unending blackness. But, to the man of faith, death is but the taking up again of the life he broke off when he came to this earth."[6]

Even those of faith may temporarily experience grief, the overwhelming sorrow that follows a loss. Losses other than death can cause grief; it is a natural reaction when we lose a home to fire, fail an important test, lose a family member to transgression, develop a debilitating illness, suffer a financial setback, lose a job, or see the disintegration of a marriage or close friendship.

We know that grief causes tremendous emotional pain. But we also know that grief can actually make people sick—and can lead to early death. That truth has been acknowledged for thousands of years. An early epitaph by Sir Henry Wootton crisply summarizes the effect that grief and bereavement can have on those who mourn:

> He first deceased; she for a little tried
> To live without him; liked it not, and died.[7]

Grief, wrote psychologist David Tubesing, "is the process of healing from the pain of loss. The process is as natural and predictable as the formation of a scab on a cut and the subsequent itching that signals healing."[8] Dr. Elisabeth Kübler-Ross identified six normal stages of grief:

- *Denial,* a disbelief that the loss has actually occurred
- *Anger* over the loss
- *Bargaining,* an attempt to reverse the loss by offering something in exchange (the bargaining usually occurs with God)
- *Depression,* feeling intense sorrow over the loss
- *Acceptance* of the loss
- *Hope* for the future

Even normal grief can cause illness because it involves such intense emotions and because it is so inseparably connected to loss. The best protections are to allow adequate time for grieving and healing and to affirm and acknowledge the feelings that occur with grief.

Because it is a process of healing, grief is necessary; but grief that is prolonged, incomplete, or abnormal can cause serious psychological and physical problems. So how long does "normal" grieving take? The length of time varies, just as the people who experience grief differ. One thing is certain: it may take much longer than experts originally thought: one researcher who has studied the grief process says that "a person can grieve continuously for a loved one for as long as two years, and intermittently for many years after. There is nothing wrong or unhealthy about it."[9]

The important factor seems to be the *type* of grief, not the *duration* of grief. *Bereavement* is a special kind of grief. It has been described as the process of intense and prolonged "disbonding" from someone who played an important role in a person's life and who is now gone. Researchers at the National Institute of Mental Health say that "the bereaved are very likely to be susceptible to serious illness and even death. . . . Some studies suggest a link between bereavement and specific diseases such as cancer, heart disease, and ulcers."[10]

A decade ago a prominent psychologist maintained that every death has as least two victims. The surviving "victim," the one who is left behind, is at significantly higher risk for a number of health problems than those who are not bereaved. Several factors help determine how profoundly bereavement affects a survivor. Research shows that the more people talk about a death, the fewer health problems they have during the year following the death—possibly because the more they talk about the death, the less they think about it, which reduces the risk of health problems.[11]

The risk of health problems from bereavement also depends in part on age. Although divorce takes a greater toll for older people, the harmful effects of widowhood are greater at younger ages. The younger a person is when a spouse dies, the greater the likelihood that health problems or premature death will follow.[12]

The risk of health problems also seems to depend partly on how swiftly the spouse dies; even then there are differences in the ways men and women react. Research conducted at the University of Utah and sponsored by the National Institute on Aging showed that women fare better when a husband dies suddenly, and men do better when a wife dies of a chronic illness.

The profound health effects of bereavement, however, are no respecter of persons: both men and women are affected. One reason may be the deterioration of social support for both men and women that can occur following divorce or the death of a spouse.

The network of support available through Relief Society, priesthood quorums, visiting teaching, home teaching, and attendance at church meetings becomes even more important for the divorced and widowed.

For both men and women, an entire host of symptoms and illnesses appear more frequently among the bereaved. The most common symptoms associated with bereavement are headaches, dizziness, fainting spells, skin rashes, excessive sweating, indigestion, difficulty swallowing, and chest pain.[13]

Researchers say there's a logical reason why the bereaved have more health problems than usual: bereavement can seriously affect the immune system. Australian researchers who took blood samples from people after the death of a spouse found that there were major drops in the activity of immune cells.[14] Other research shows that during periods of active mourning, the body produces far too much of a stress hormone that prevents the immune system from kicking completely into gear.[15]

One reason for a drop in immune function during bereavement is the brain. As one researcher said, "The heart cannot decide that a loved one's death in a train wreck is too much to bear; the liver does not feel the shame of embarrassment; the immune system does not know whether its client is employed or not, divorced or happily married. It is the brain that knows and feels."[16]

Besides its effect on the immune system, bereavement has also been linked to several specific health effects. We've all heard about people who "died of a broken heart." According to research, there may be a lot of truth to the saying. Consider, for example, that heart attack rates of widows between the ages of twenty-five and thirty-four is *five times* that of married women in the same age group.[17] A startling number of premature deaths have been linked to bereavement, and researchers have found that almost half of all deaths during the first six months are due to heart problems. One reason may be that bereavement speeds the development of arteriosclerotic heart disease, "a process that usually develops at an imperceptibly slow pace over a period of decades."[18]

In fact, research shows that loss, grief, mourning, and bereavement themselves can and do cause sudden death. One of the most notable researchers in the field, Dr. George Engle of New York's Rochester University Medical School, studied cases of sudden death in which he could reconstruct the circumstances surrounding the death. In more than half the sudden deaths he investigated, Engle was able to document that the death was immediately preceded by some kind of profound loss. Most often, the deaths occurred after the collapse or death of a loved one, during the sixteen days following the loss or during the threat of loss of a loved one.[19] And these deaths don't happen just to the elderly; they often involve young, apparently healthy people who suddenly and unexpectedly lose someone close to them.

When all causes of death are considered, the bereaved have a much higher death rate than people of the same age whose spouses are living. The increased death rate is sharpest during the first months; during the first week alone, mortality rates in one study doubled for both men and women. Widows die at rates three to thirteen times married women for every known major cause of death.[20] And both men and women who lose their mates are among the highest risk groups for premature death.

And what of loneliness? "The most devastating of all human emotions," proclaimed Elder Sterling W. Sill, "is this sense of being alone, or not being wanted, or being unworthy." It is a "terrible loneliness," he said, that "haunts the minds and hearts of people in this life."[21]

Loneliness does not necessarily accompany loss. History provides richly illustrated examples of the most profound kind of loneliness. Joseph felt dulling isolation as he was sold into Egypt. Jacob described his as a "lonesome and solemn people, wanderers, cast out from Jerusalem, born in tribulation, in a wilderness, and hated of our brethren . . . wherefore, we did mourn out our days" (Jacob 7:26). John the Baptist lived in astute isolation and loneliness throughout his life. The Prophet Joseph Smith languished in a cramped, dank limestone cell in Liberty Jail.

And ponder the Savior, who as a boy of twelve stood alone among the learned in the temple; who in the isolation of a mountaintop faced the piercing temptation of the adversary; who without human companionship bore a grief beyond utterance in the heavy shadows of Gethsemane. And there was the absolute and excruciating loneliness of Golgotha, when the Savior cried in agony, "My God, my God, why hast thou forsaken me?" (Matthew 27:46). There is, as Elder Neal A. Maxwell once told us, nothing we can tell the Savior about loneliness.

Mortality involves a certain amount of physical discomfort and suffering: hunger, disease, exposure, and trauma. There are also certain emotional conditions—anxiety, sorrow, despair, rejection—which can be more intense and painful than the physical ills that befall us. Among them is loneliness.

Loneliness has nothing to do with how many people are around. We can, as the popular saying goes, be "lonely in a crowd." Researchers believe that loneliness comes not from the number of relationships in our lives, but the amount of fulfillment we get from those relationships.[22] It has to do with whether our expectations of life are met and whether we *perceive* ourselves to be isolated.

Not many conditions rival the pain of loneliness. One writer said that "the most horrible punishment that could be inflicted upon you is not twenty years of hard labor, but twenty years of solitary confinement." Loneliness seems to be on the increase, and numerous factors are involved. More people than ever are living alone; four times as many people live alone today as did in the 1950s. The divorce rate is rising, and there is a trend away from marriage. Mobility is increasing; almost half the U.S. population relocates within any five-year period, and one in five people changes residence every year in this country. In many ways, the individual is replacing the family as the basic unit of American society.[23]

There are other factors contributing to the loneliness trend: fewer face-to-face business transactions are completed. An increased amount of banking is done at automated teller machines. Computers write letters, make telephone calls, and handle financial transactions. People sit alone in front of the television set and video machine instead of going out into the community to watch movies, attend the theater, or patronize the arts. Larger cities have become particularly impersonal as high crime rates have discouraged people from leaving home to socialize.[24]

Personal characteristics and cultural values can also bring loneliness. Two age risks are at greater risk for loneliness: the elderly (whose spouse, loved ones, and friends begin to die) and teenagers (who tend to have unrealistic expectations about what friendships should involve). Other risk factors for loneliness include lower income, gender (women are more likely to form deep and intimate relationships), and a family structure in which parents are isolated.

Loneliness causes not only emotional and spiritual emptiness, but it hurts our physical health as well. A possible reason why is that loneliness causes people to release the same hormones that are released during stress; when loneliness is combined with stress, the results can be especially devastating.

Loneliness seems to have a particular impact on the health of the heart. There may be a physical reason: loneliness causes changes in the nervous and endocrine systems that lead to atherosclerosis, a hardening of the arteries that leads to heart disease.[25] In the largest study yet to determine the effect of loneliness on the heart, researchers from Johns Hopkins School of Public Health and Sweden's Karolinska Institute studied more than seventeen thousand Swedes for six years. Even after allowing for other health risks, the people who were loneliest had a forty percent greater risk of dying from heart disease than the rest of the people in the study.[26] In one of the most comprehensive studies of disease and premature death, researchers studied fifty thousand former students of the University of Pennsylvania and Harvard University. The students who were the loneliest and most socially isolated were most at risk to die of heart disease.[27]

A number of studies have also correlated loneliness with unusually high incidences of cancer. A significant study that showed the link between loneliness and cancer was done at the

Johns Hopkins University School of Medicine. Researchers collected psychological data on nearly a thousand men who had attended medical school and then followed them for twenty-five years. Medical records were carefully examined. One in five of the "loners"—students who felt lonely and faced the world with bland, unemotional exteriors—developed cancer, a rate twenty times higher than for some of the other students in the study.[28]

Available data from hundreds of in-depth studies points to lack of human companionship, chronic loneliness, and social isolation as "among the leading causes of premature death."[29] Samuel Silverman, associate clinical professor of psychiatry at Harvard University, claims a person can add up to fifteen years to life simply by reducing two "emotional aging factors," one of which is loneliness.

How can we ease loneliness and prevent it from making you sick? One way is through a change in attitude—by determining what it *means* to be lonely. Being alone doesn't dictate loneliness. Anne Morrow Lindbergh wrote in *Gift from the Sea:*

> I find there is a quality to being alone that is incredibly precious. Life rushes back into the void, richer, more vivid, fuller than before. It is as if in parting one did actually lose an arm. And then, like starfish, one grows it anew; one is whole again, complete and round—more whole, even, than before, when the other people had pieces of one.[30]

We can accomplish many things in those moments of solitude that we can't accomplish at any other time. As Elder Neal A. Maxwell wrote, "solitude can have its uses. I sometimes wonder if, in fact, such moments are not designed precisely in order to focus us upon God—to show us our utter dependence on Him. Otherwise, the cares of the world will call the cadence."[31]

Another way to ease loneliness is, of course, through the comfort and companionship of a friend. Friends contribute to health by providing all the functions of the family, and they help mold our sense of esteem. Friends help buffer the harmful effects of stress, and provide a natural outlet for confiding feelings. Researchers have found that openly discussing a traumatic event with someone else can actually improve physical health, even when the traumatic event occurred many years earlier.[32]

Another way of easing loneliness is having a pet. Research into the benefits of pet ownership has shown beyond a doubt that comfort does not always have to come only from people.[33] Pets provide companionship, make us feel safe, help us feel calm, and are a constant amid the change. One of the greatest health benefits of pets is their effect on the heart. Researchers found that among patients hospitalized for heart disease, pet owners had one-third the death rate of people who did not own pets. There is a scientific reason for this: patients have lower heart rates when they are with their pets, and pets help reduce blood pressure. Petting a dog will lower blood pressure among healthy college students, hospitalized elderly, and even adults with chronic high blood pressure. The blood pressure of bird owners dropped an average of ten points when they were talking to their birds. And watching fish in an aquarium brought blood pressure to below resting levels.[34]

The Church itself provides ample opportunities for involvement that, if taken advantage of, can help to ease loneliness. Attendance at meetings, participation in activities, and faithful exercise of the home teaching and visiting teaching programs can draw out those who have difficulty meeting others. Extending the hand of friendship and fellowship is a prescribed gospel activity. We are told that those who join the Church are "no more strangers . . . but fellowcitizens" (Ephesians 2:19).

Finally, one of the surest antidotes to loneliness is the gospel of Jesus Christ and the knowledge it gives us of our relative position in the world. President Brigham Young told the early Saints, "We are not here isolated and alone, differently formed and composed of different material than the rest of the human race. We belong to and are part of this family."[35]

These are similar to the ways that can help you cut the health risks of grief and bereavement. One of the best ways is to surround yourself with people who are supportive; begin with the network in your own ward and stake, and move outward from there. People who perceive that their social support is strong reap protective health benefits as a result. One way to overcome bereavement is to focus on people, experiences, and emotions other than the loss. Another is to cling to the comfort of religious faith. Prayer allies us with the Savior, who has promised that "I will not leave you comfortless: I will come to you" (John 14:18).

The gospel of Jesus Christ, taught President Thomas S. Monson, is the "penetrating light that makes of every hopeless dawn a joyful morning."[36] The Lord himself counseled us, "If thou art sorrowful, call on the Lord thy God with supplication, that your souls may be joyful" (D&C 136:29). President Ezra Taft Benson taught that "prayer in the hour of need is a great boon. From simple trials to our Gethsemanes, prayer can put us in touch with God, our greatest source of comfort and counsel."[37]

The Savior himself has issued the invitation: "Come unto me, all ye that labour and are heavy laden, and I will give you rest. For my yoke is easy, and my burden is light" (Matthew 11: 28, 30). We will experience loss. Grief will follow, But though we face sorrow, fear, disappointment, and bereavement, he is always there for us, and his help is always available. And, most important, his atoning sacrifice includes all of us and assures us of a life to come with those we have loved and lost.

As Elder Neal A. Maxwell so eloquently wrote:

> Awaiting the faithful is God's greatest gift of all—eternal life (D&C 14:7)—for which all humans will have had an equal chance to strive. The gift of immortality to all is so choice a gift that our rejoicing in these two great and generous gifts should drown out any sorrow, assuage any grief, conquer any mood, dissolve any despair, and tame any tragedy.
>
> Even those who see life as pointless will one day point with adoration to the performance of the Man of Galilee in the crowded moments of time known as Gethsemane and

> Calvary. Those who now say life is meaningless will yet applaud the atonement, which saved us all from meaninglessness. . . .
>
> A disciple's "brightness of hope," therefore, means that at funerals his tears are not because of termination, but because of interruption and separation. Though just as wet, his tears are not of despair, but of appreciation and anticipation. Yes, for disciples, the closing of a grave is but the closing of a door that will later be flung open.
>
> It is the Garden Tomb, not life, that is empty![38]

We who have the gospel have the solution for the bitter loneliness that grips so much of mankind. "The answers men so much seek are to be found," concluded Elder Richard L. Evans, "and to the aching, yearning loneliness of human hearts, and to the anguished agony of the world there can come direction, revelation, comfort, guidance, inspiration, and a finding of the way to the purposeful, happy living of life . . . with the blessed assurance of an everlasting life with limitless opportunities, and with our loved ones with us."[39]

END NOTES

1. Edward L. Kimball, compiler, *The Teachings of Spencer W. Kimball* (Salt Lake City: Bookcraft, 1982), p. 9.
2. Bruce R. McConkie, *Doctrinal New Testament Commentary: The Gospels,* Vol. 1 (Salt Lake City: Bookcraft, 1966), pp. 774-75.
3. James E. Talmage, *Jesus the Christ,* 15th edition, revised (Salt Lake City: The Church of Jesus Christ of Latter-day Saints, 1977), p. 669.
4. Hugh Nibley, *The World and the Prophets: Collected Works of Hugh Nibley,* Vol. 3 (Salt Lake City: Deseret Book, and Provo, Utah: Foundation for Ancient Research and Mormon Studies, 1987), p. 259.
5. Bruce R. McConkie, *A New Witness for the Articles of Faith* (Salt Lake City: Deseret Book, 1985), pp. 704-705.
6. James R. Clark, ed., *Messages of the First Presidency of The Church of Jesus Christ of Latter-day Saints,* Vol. 6 (Salt Lake City: Bookcraft, 1975), p. 32.

7. Wolfgang Stroebe and Margaret S. Stroebe, *Bereavement and Health* (Cambridge, Mass.: Cambridge University Press, 1987), p. 1.
8. Emrika Padus, *The Complete Guide to Your Health and Emotions* (Emmaus, Penn.: Rodale Press, 1986), p. 156.
9. Sharon Faelten, David Diamon, and the editors of *Prevention* magazine, *Take Control of Your Life: A Complete Guide to Stress Relief* (Emmaus, Penn.: Rodale Press, 1988), p. 134.
10. "NIMH Issues Guides to Bereavement," *Behavior Today,* November 7, 1988, p. 3.
11. James W. Pennebaker and Joan R. Susman, "Disclosure of Traumas and Psychosomatic Processes," *Social Science Medicine*, Vol. 26, No. 3, 1988, pp. 327-32.
12. Sheldon Cohen and S. Leonard Syme, *Social Support and Health* (Orlando, Fla.: Academic Press, Inc., 1985).
13. Wolfgang Stroebe and Margaret S. Stroebe, *Bereavement and Health* (Cambridge, Mass.: Cambridge University Press, 1987), p. 143.
14. Blair Justice, *Who Gets Sick: Thinking and Health* (Houston, Tex.: Peak Press, 1987), p. 188.
15. Marc Pilisuk and Susan Hillier Parks, *The Healing Web* (Hanover, N.H.: the University of New England Press, 1986), p. 33.
16. Robert Ornstein and David Sobel, "The Healing Brain," *Psychology Today,* March 1987, pp. 48-52.
17. James J. Lynch, *The Broken Heart: The Medical Consequences of Loneliness* (New York: Basic Books, Inc., 1977), p. 76.
18. Ibid.
19. Ibid., p. 77.
20. Claudia Wallis, "Stress: Can We Cope?" *Time,* June 6, 1983, pp. 48-54.
21. Sterling W. Sill, *Brigham Young University Speeches of the Year* (Provo, Utah: BYU Press, 1960), p. 13.
22. Larry Dossey, *Meaning and Medicine: A Doctor's Tales of Breakthrough and Healing* (New York: Bantam Books, 1991), pp. 71-72.
23. Marc Pilisuk and Susan Hillier Parks, *The Healing Web* (Hanover, N.H.: The University Press of New England, 1986), p. 65.
24. Carin Rubenstein and Phillip Shaver, "Are You Lonely? How to Find Intimacy, Love, and Happiness," *Shape,* August 1987, p. 72.

25. The editors of *Prevention* magazine, *Positive Living and Health: The Complete Guide to Brain/Body Healing and Mental Empowerment* (Emmaus, Penn.: Rodale Press, 1990), p. 154.
26. Alix Kerr, "Hearts Need Friends," from *Physician's Weekly.*
27. James J. Lynch, *The Broken Heart: The Medical Consequences of Loneliness* (New York: Basic Books, Inc., Publishers, 1977).
28. Eleanor Smith, "Fighting Cancerous Feelings," *Psychology Today,* May 1988, pp. 22-23.
29. Sharon Faelten, David Diamond, and the editors of *Prevention* magazine, *Take Control of Your Life: A Complete Guide to Stress Relief* (Emmaus, Penn.: Rodale Press, 1988), p. 58.
30. Anne Morrow Lindbergh, *Gift from the Sea* (New York: Pantheon Books, 1955), p. 42.
31. Neal A. Maxwell, *We Talk of Christ, We Rejoice in Christ* (Salt Lake City: Deseret Book, 1984), p. 47.
32. J. W. Pennebaker, et al., "Friends and Loneliness," *Psychosomatic Medicine* 51, 1989, p. 577.
33. Robert Ornstein and Charles Swencionis, *The Healing Brain: A Scientific Reader* (New York: The Guilford Press, 1990), p. 93.
34. Lynne Lohmeier, "The Healing Power of Pets," *East/West,* June 1988, p. 52.
35. John A. Widtsoe, compiler, *Discourses of Brigham Young* (Salt Lake City: Deseret Book, 1978), p. 271.
36. Thomas S. Monson, *Conference Report,* April 1976, p. 16.
37. Ezra Taft Benson, *Conference Report,* October 1974, p. 91.
38. Neal A. Maxwell, *Wherefore, Ye Must Press Forward* (Salt Lake City: Deseret Book, 1977), pp. 132-33.
39. Richard L. Evans, *Conference Report,* October 1963, p. 44.

Solitude can have its uses.

— Neal A. Maxwell

Service with all our heart and mind is a high challenge for all of us. Such service must be free of selfish ambition. It must be motivated only by the pure love of Christ.

— DALLIN H. OAKS

CHAPTER

8

Serving Others

Altruism—the act of giving oneself out of a genuine concern for other people—has been called one of the healthiest of human attributes. Physician and philosopher Albert Schweitzer proclaimed that the only people who will be truly happy "are those who will have sought and found how to serve." German-born physicist and Nobel Prize winner Albert Einstein said, "Only a life lived for others is worth living."

The scriptures admonish us that the only true way to find ourselves is to lose ourselves in service to others. In the Doctrine and Covenants, we read about how important it is to "succor the weak, lift up the hands which hang down, and strengthen the feeble knees" (D&C 81:5). And we are told that Christ, the greatest leader ever born, was also the greatest servant of all (see Mark 10:44).

Altruism is part of our history as human beings; it is a central theme in the universe. "When the first cell divided to form two cells, when it gave up its life for two others, we have the beginnings of true altruism," one philosopher noted. "Altruism is the very nature of living matter . . . an integral part of life."[1] Service may, in fact, be an essential part of life itself. "Service is the one thing required of every soul," wrote Joseph Fielding Smith. "He who will not serve his fellows is not fit to have place among them. . . . No man is independent. Put a man off by himself where he could communicate with none of his fellow beings or receive aid from them, and he would perish miserably."[2]

The history of the Church is a history of selfless service. Journals are replete with examples like the one of George Coates, who lost four of his family members during the influenza epidemic of 1918. Within a day or two of what was a stunning loss, he was faced with the task of digging as much as he could of his beet crop before the ground froze any more solid. Pulling through their grief, he and several of his sons climbed aboard a wagon drawn by four horses and started toward the field. As his son remembers:

> As they drove along the Saratoga Road, they passed wagon after wagon-load of beets being hauled to the factory and driven by neighborhood farmers. As they passed by, each driver would wave a greeting: "Hi ya, Uncle George," "Sure sorry, George," "Tough break, George," "You've got a lot of friends, George."
>
> On the last wagon was the town comedian, freckled-faced Jasper Rolfe. He waved a cheery greeting and called out: "That's all of 'em, Uncle George."
>
> My dad turned to Francis and said: "I wish it was all of ours."
>
> When they arrived at the farm gate, Francis jumped down off the big red beet wagon and opened the gate as we drove onto the field. He pulled up, stopped the team, and paused a moment and scanned the field, from left to right and back and forth—and lo and behold, there wasn't a sugar beet on the whole field. Then it dawned on him what Jasper Rolfe meant when he called out: "That's all of 'em, Uncle George!"
>
> Then dad got down off the wagon, picked up a handful of the rich, brown soil he loved so much, and then in this thumbless left hand a beet top, and he looked for a

> moment at these symbols of his labor as if he couldn't believe his eyes.
>
> Then father sat down on a pile of beet tops—this man who brought four of his loved ones home for burial in the course of only six days; made caskets, dug graves, and even helped with the burial clothing—this amazing man who never faltered, nor flinched, nor wavered throughout this amazing ordeal—sat down on a pile of beet tops and sobbed like a little child.
>
> Then he arose, wiped his eyes with his big, red bandanna handkerchief, looked up at the sky, and said: "Thanks, Father, for the elders of our ward."[3]

That kind of service continues. And today, the Church encourages active volunteerism among its members in local, national, and international causes; for example, Church members contributed nearly $11 million for famine relief and agricultural development in Ethiopia in 1985. And the LDS Church is one of the most active sponsors of the Boy Scouts in the United States.

The Church itself is a model of altruism and unselfish service. Wards and stakes worldwide are staffed by Church members who voluntarily donate their time and talents for others. Church leaders willingly help meet the physical, spiritual, and emotional needs of those in their care. Tens of thousands of missionaries spend their own time and resources to share the gospel. And members throughout the world fill the temples to capacity daily for the redemption of the dead. No one is paid, but such volunteer work is a priority in a church that embraces charity, love, and joy through service as basic tenets of a Christ-centered life.

Church doctrine emphasizes the importance of altruism. Service, wrote Elder Bruce R. McConkie, "is essential to salvation. . . . Not only must mortals keep the commandments to gain an inheritance in the Father's kingdom, but they must also get outside themselves in service to their fellowmen."[4]

It is not only the recipient of service that is blessed, but the one who renders service as well. Service clothed in charity—the pure love of Christ—becomes a rewarding experience for both giver and receiver. "We can't help others without helping ourselves," taught President Ezra Taft Benson. In addition to blessing us with happiness, personal growth, and the things of the spirit, he said, service allows us to "achieve a measure of faithfulness and worthiness that will enable us, when our time comes, to stride ahead into the eternities to come."[5]

Service develops within us the attitudes we need to thrive in a day when, as prophesied, the earth is in commotion and the love of many waxes cold. And the introspection that accompanies service becomes yet another blessing to those who serve. President Spencer W. Kimball taught:

> Service puts problems in perspective. I have learned that it is by serving that we learn how to serve. When we are engaged in the service of our fellowmen, not only do our deeds assist them, but we put our own problems in a fresher perspective. When we concern ourselves more with others, there is less time to be concerned with ourselves. In the midst of the miracle of serving, there is the promise of Jesus, that by losing ourselves, we find ourselves. Not only do we "find" ourselves in terms of acknowledging guidance in our lives, but the more we serve our fellowmen in appropriate ways, the more substance there is to our souls.[6]

But the benefits of service aren't restricted to the spiritual. The ability to connect to others by placing their needs above our own also appears to contribute to a longer and healthier life. Scientists are beginning to conclude that doing good for others is good for us, especially for the nervous system and the immune system. The result of research at Harvard University shows that genuine altruism may be so powerful that even *thinking* about altruistic action may give your immune system a boost.[7]

Altruism may boost immunity because it reduces stress through social contact and a sense of purpose. We know that stress depresses immunity by reducing the activity of natural killer cells and reducing the number and activity of white blood cells. There are also changes in the normal ratio of immune system cells that keep the system operating as it should.[8] Not only does altruism reduce stress, but the positive emotions related to altruism, such as love and compassion, help stabilize the immune system against the effects of stress.

Harvard cardiologist Herbert Benson, well-known for his research on the effects of relaxation, says that helping others works much the same way as yoga, spirituality, and meditation. Research shows that helping others reduces blood pressure, slows down the heart rate, and causes other benefits to health.[9]

Varied research shows that helping others causes the brain to release endorphins, powerful natural painkillers that literally make us feel better and that help relieve stress. In fact, women in two major studies about volunteerism described a "helper's high" similar in nature to the "runner's high" people experience when exercising.[10] Allan Luks, executive director of the Institute for the Advancement of Health in New York City, says that "people who help others frequently report better health than people who don't help." People who consistently render service, says Luks, have a greater sense of well-being and fewer stress-related health problems.[11]

Luks paired up with a psychologist at New York State Psychiatric Institute to study the "helper's high" more closely. They found that what they call the "healthy helper syndrome" actually has two separate effects: one immediate (an initial physical "high," most likely caused by endorphins), and a second, longer-lasting sense of calm and heightened emotional well-being. The combined effect is a powerful antidote for stress, a key to happiness and optimism, and a way to combat feelings of helplessness and depression.[12]

The survey showed something else, too: the more often people volunteered or served others, the greater the health benefits. Those who consistently served others once a week reported ten times better health. They also noticed specific improvements in their health, including less pain, fewer common colds, less-frequent migraine headaches, fewer asthma attacks, and less-frequent bouts of flu. And those good feelings last far beyond the act of service itself; almost eighty percent of those studied said the good feelings kept recurring long after the service had actually ended.[13]

There are several reasons why people who volunteer and serve others have better health. According to researchers, volunteers have stronger immune systems, more endorphins (which relieve pain), more positive emotions (which help maintain good health), fewer harmful emotions (like hostility and anger), and greater stress relief.[14] Additionally, people who serve others tend to be optimistic, an important health-preserving quality. Psychologist Martin Seligman says that altruism "presupposes a belief that things can change for the better,"and he maintains that optimists "have better health, better immune systems, and so live longer."[15]

A group of studies done on altruism found that people who care for others are physically, emotionally, and mentally healthier than those who concentrate more on their own needs. Many researchers believe that altruism is an inborn characteristic intended to help boost health and longevity. One of them, bioethic researcher Willard Gaylin, says, "We are born with a natural caring tendency. I don't think it's so rare. We take care of infants who certainly do nothing to deserve it. They're not attractive. They wake you in the middle of the night. They urinate on you. They vomit on you. And yet we love them and care for them."

One of the most profound examples of the health and longevity benefits of serving others comes from the life of philanthropist John D. Rockefeller, Sr.[16] Rockefeller entered the business world with gusto and drove himself so hard that he had earned his first million dollars by age thirty-three. Ten years later he owned and controlled the world's largest business. By the time he was fifty-three, he was the world's first billionaire.

But he had crushed countless people in his pursuit of wealth—and they hated him. Workers in Pennsylvania's oil fields hanged him in effigy. He was guarded day and night by bodyguards pledged to protect his life. He developed alopecia, a condition in which all body hair falls out. His digestion was so poor that all he could eat was crackers and milk. He couldn't sleep at night. The doctors who struggled to help him agreed that he wouldn't live another year.

Then something happened to John D. Rockefeller. He began to think of—and care about—others more than he did himself. He decided to use his billions of dollars for the benefit of others. Through the Rockefeller Foundation, he gave hundreds of millions of dollars to hospitals, universities, missions, and private citizens. Money he donated helped in the discovery of penicillin. His contributions to medicine enabled researchers to find cures for tuberculosis, malaria, diphtheria, and many other diseases that had robbed so many of life. His contributions also helped rid the southern United States of its greatest physical and economic plague, the hookworm.

When Rockefeller started using his riches to help other people, he helped himself. For the first time in years, he was able to eat normally. He felt renewed. He slept soundly. He defied the odds and lived to see his fifty-fourth birthday—and many birthdays after that. In fact, he kept on giving and caring for others until he died at the age of ninety-eight.

In essence, the health benefits of altruism and volunteer service may depend on the driving emotion behind it all: love, a projection of one's own good feelings onto other people. Those who become more loving and less fearful and who replace negative thoughts with the positive emotion of love are often able to achieve physical healing. For example, people faced with life-threatening illness are often overcome with fear—fear of pain, fear of the future, fear of death. Fear can drain the ability to heal and can incapacitate a person. Once love becomes the overriding emotion, however, great changes can take place. "What we're talking about is love," says one researcher. "That's where the power is. Once you tap into it, you have joined up with a universal energy force. And with that power, nothing is impossible."[17]

Although we don't fully understand the physiological effects of love, there is much we do know. One of the most important effects is a boost of the immune system. Harvard psychologist David McClelland has shown that love improves white blood cell function and improves overall resistance to disease.[18] Tests conducted at the Meninger Clinic in Topeka, Kansas, showed that love makes white blood cells significantly more active in fighting infection. People who expressed love had fewer colds, had lower levels of lactic acid in their blood (which means they were less likely to get tired), and had higher levels of endorphins in their blood (which made them feel good and relieved pain).[19]

Scores of studies point out the importance of love to good health.[20] In one, people who were isolated had two to three times the risk of death from heart disease and all other causes. In another, people who felt loved and supported developed much less atherosclerosis of the coronary arteries (a major risk factor for heart disease). In still another, elderly adults who felt loved and supported had lower cholesterol levels and better immune function.

"The mandate to 'Love your neighbor as you love yourself' is not just a moral mandate. It's a physiological mandate," wrote University of Maryland School of Medicine researcher James Lynch. "Caring is biological. One thing you get from caring for others is you're not lonely. And the more connected you are to life, the healthier you are."[21]

Many believe that the tendency toward altruism is established early in life. Psychologist Alfie Kohn noted that altruism may be as dramatic as donating a kidney or "as mundane as letting another shopper ahead of you in line. But most of us do it frequently and started doing it very early in life. . . . Caring about others is as much a part of human nature as caring about ourselves."[22]

There are plenty of things we can all do to be of service. Too often we focus only on formal activities, such as a service project organized by the Relief Society or a Boy Scout project. Elder Neal A. Maxwell points out that these are "surely needed and commendable," but "quiet, personal service is also urgently needed. . . . In serving, as in true worship, we need to do some things together and some things personally. Our spiritual symmetry is our own responsibility, and balance is so important."[23] The most important service we offer may not always be the most grandiose, either. As President Spencer W. Kimball taught, "So often, our acts of service consist of simple encouragement or of giving mundane help with mundane tasks, but what glorious consequences can flow from mundane acts and from small but deliberate deeds!"[24]

Some opportunities for individual service are obvious: a parent's service to a child, a child who cares for a parent, a parent who gives up outside interests to create a quality home life, a home teacher or visiting teacher who approaches that calling with insight and concern, a neighbor who takes dinner to a new mother. Some of the most effective kinds of service may not be so obvious:

> So often what parched and thirsty people need is to be . . . revived by the food of fellowship. Giving genuine companionship to the malnourished mortals who have known so little love and so few friends is as vital as food for the starving.
>
> So often we can serve by bathing the wounded and bruised egos of others in the warm water of deserved commendation.
>
> So often what people need is to be enveloped in the raiment of real response.
>
> So often what people need so much is to be sheltered from the storms of life in the sanctuary of belonging.[25]

Regardless of the times, and regardless of our own circumstances, one of the vital things we must do is to keep serving, an activity, says Elder Neal A. Maxwell, that will provide "some of our most choice mortal experiences."[26]

Opportunities abound. As President Gordon B. Hinckley explained, there are "so many out there whose burdens you can lift. There are the homeless, there are the hungry, there are the destitute all around us. There are the aged who are alone in rest homes. There are handicapped children, and youth on drugs, and the sick and the homebound who cry out for a kind word."[27]

From King Benjamin's powerful sermon on service, we learn that, ultimately, our need to serve comes full circle from our dependence on the Lord:

> For behold, are we not all beggars? Do we not all depend upon the same Being, even God, for all the substance which we have . . . ?
>
> And now, if God, who has created you, on whom you are dependent for your lives and for all that ye have and are, doth grant unto you whatsoever ye ask that is right, in faith, believing that ye shall receive, O then, how ye ought to impart of the substance that ye have one to another. (Mosiah 4:19, 21)

END NOTES

1. G. B. Gutten, *Instincts and Religion* (New York: Harper and Brothers, 1940), p. 43.
2. Joseph Fielding Smith, Jr., *The Way to Perfection: Short Discourses on Gospel Themes,* 9th edition (Salt Lake City: The Genealogical Society of The Church of Jesus Christ of Latter-day Saints, 1951), p. 218.
3. Vaughn J. Featherstone, *Conference Report,* April 1973, pp. 46-48.
4. Bruce R. McConkie, *The Mortal Messiah* (Salt Lake City: Deseret Book, 1979), pp. 468-69.
5. Ezra Taft Benson, *Teachings of Ezra Taft Benson* (Salt Lake City: Bookcraft, 1988), pp. 449-50.
6. Spencer W. Kimball, *The Teachings of Spencer W. Kimball,* comp. by Edward L. Kimball (Salt Lake City: Bookcraft, 1982), p. 254.
7. Eileen Rockefeller Growald and Allan Luks, "Beyond Self," *American Health,* March 1988, pp. 51-53.
8. Sarah Lang, "Extend Your Hand, Extend Your Life," *Longevity,* March 1989, p. 19.
9. Allan Luks, "Helper's High," *Psychology Today,* October 1988, p. 42.
10. Ibid., p. 39.
11. Sarah Lang, "Extend Your Hand, Extend Your Life," *Longevity,* March 1989, p. 18.

12. Allan Luks with Peggy Payne, *The Healing Power of Doing Good: The Health and Spiritual Benefits of Helping Others* (New York: Ballantine Books, 1991), p. 68.
13. Howard F. Andrews, "Helping and Health: The Relationship Between Volunteer Activity and Health-Related Outcomes," *Advances,* 7(1):1990, pp. 25-34.
14. Allan Luks with Peggy Payne, *The Healing Power of Doing Good: The Health and Spiritual Benefits of Helping Others* (New York: Ballantine Books, 1991), p. 70.
15. Sarah Lang, "Extend Your Hand, Extend Your Life," *Longevity,* March 1989, p. 19.
16. S. I. McMillen, *None of These Diseases,* revised (Old Tappan, New Jersey: Fleming H. Revell Company, 1984), pp. 188-89.
17. Emrika Padus, *The Complete Guide to Your Health and Your Emotions* (Emmaus, Penn.: Rodale Press, 1986), p. 522.
18. Blair Justice, "Think Yourself Healthy," *Prevention,* June 1988, pp. 31-32, 105-108.
19. Ibid.
20. Studies summarized from Dean Ornish, *Dr. Dean Ornish's Program for Reversing Heart Disease* (New York: Random House, Inc., 1990).
21. James Lynch, *The Broken Heart: The Medical Consequences of Loneliness* (New York: Basic Books, Inc., Publishers, 1977), p. 79.
22. "Research: Altruism and Transformation," *Noetic Sciences Review,* Autumn 1990, p. 33.
23. Neal A. Maxwell, *All These Things Shall Give Thee Experience* (Salt Lake City: Deseret Book, 1980), p. 55.
24. Spencer W. Kimball, "Small Acts of Service," *Ensign,* December 1974, p. 5.
25. Neal A. Maxwell, *All These Things Shall Give Thee Experience* (Salt Lake City: Deseret Book, 1980), p. 55.
26. Ibid., p. 52.
27. Gordon B. Hinckley, "To Single Adults," *Ensign,* June 1989, p. 73.

Wo Unto Them That Put Bitter for Sweet

The rain descended and the floods came and the winds blew and beat upon the house which was built upon the rock with the same force as that which destroyed the other house. This house did not escape the storm but, having a rock foundation, withstood it. Both the storms of nature and the storms of life are indiscriminate. As the house built upon the rock survived the storm, so the life whose roots are firmly planted in the soil of faith will endure adversity and be made stronger by the struggle.

— HUGH B. BROWN

CHAPTER

9

The Impact of Stress on Health

Stress occurs whenever there is a change and we are forced to adapt to that change; scientifically speaking, it's anything that challenges the body's internal sense of balance. Whether we call it adversity or affliction or stress, no one can escape it, nor would we want to. As Elder H. Burke Peterson reminded us, "trials are an evidence of a Father's love."[1]

Elder B. H. Roberts wrote that "the paths that lead into the deepest valleys of sorrow and up to the most rugged steps of adversity are the ones which if a man travel in, will best accomplish the object of his existence in this world."[2]

The contrast between a life filled with adversity and one relatively free from stress is compelling; Elder Roberts compares it to the contrast between a mountain stream and a stagnant pool. The stream, which is dashed against rocks and tumbles through rugged canyons, keeps its waters pure. The pool, on the other hand, rests but is sluggish, overgrown and infested with filth. So it is, wrote Elder Roberts, with the life of man:

> The conditions which place men where they may always walk on the unbroken plain of prosperity and seek for nothing but their own pleasure, are not the best within the gift of God. For in such circumstances men soon drop into a position analogous to the stagnant pool; while those who have to contend with difficulties, brave dangers, endure disappointments, struggle with sorrows, eat the bread of adversity and drink the water of affliction, develop a moral and spiritual strength, together with a purity of life and character, unknown to the heirs of ease. . . .[3]

In speaking of our experience in mortality, Elder Neal A. Maxwell wrote, "Into the brief, fleeting time allotted to each of us must be crowded challenges that will help us, in our weaknesses, to develop the qualities we now lack. The presence of stress may be needed for their development. Otherwise, the adversary could taunt us as he did Job by saying that an insulated Job was an untested Job."[4]

We, like Job, will have the opportunity to experience stress and adversity. And we will have the chance to react as did Job, who, when faced with adversity, cried, "Naked came I out of my mother's womb, and naked shall I return thither: the Lord gave, and the Lord hath taken away; blessed be the name of the Lord" (Job 1:21).

"There are those who have met disaster," said President David O. McKay, "which almost seems defeat, who have become somewhat soured in their natures, but if they stop to think, even the adversity which has come to them may prove a means of spiritual uplift. Adversity itself may lead toward and not away from God and spiritual enlightenment; and privation may prove a source of strength if we can but keep a sweetness of mind and spirit."[5]

"Do we really want immunity from adversity? Especially when certain kinds of suffering can aid our growth in this life?" asks Elder Maxwell. "To deprive ourselves of those experiences, much as we might momentarily like to, would be to deprive ourselves of the outcomes over which we shouted with anticipated joy when this life's experiences were explained to us so long ago, in the world before we came here."[6]

Obviously, we *want* and *need* some degree of stress and adversity in our lives. Modern-day revelation assures us that stress and adversity mold us into the kind of men and women we ultimately hope to be. But too much stress can make us sick; at an extreme, it can even cut short our lives. Are the two at odds? Is there contradiction between the laboratory of science and that of the spirit?

No! Stress *will* happen. Stress *is* a necessary part of our lives. And stress *can* make us sick. But the way we perceive stress and our ability to cope with it can make us strong, not sick. Attitudes, beliefs, and perceptions help keep us well. Ample evidence, cited throughout this book, shows how spiritual factors like optimism, faith, and hope can help overcome the devastating physical effects of stress.

Yale surgeon Bernie S. Siegel, well known for his research on the link between behavior and disease, points out that "stresses we *choose* evoke a [physical] response totally different from those we'd like to avoid but cannot. Helplessness is worse than the stress itself."[7] Stresses we choose—we may call them "challenges"—give us a sense of controlled excitement, like the skillful descent of a steep ski slope. Those we do not choose can leave us feeling out of control, like a passenger in a runaway train.

Stress can either be threatening or challenging; its consequences can contribute either to personal growth or to despair. Those outcomes are independent of our physical health. How will we fare? Leonard Sagan, internationally respected for his study of disease, maintains that two factors determine whether stress makes us sick. One is the magnitude of the stress itself, something we can't control. The other factor, however, is squarely within our control: it is "the capacity of the individual to cope."[8]

Much of our ability to resist the harmful effects of stress, to endure, has to do with perception. The gospel of Jesus Christ encourages us to look at challenges as one more blessing given us by a loving Father, not as punishment for some misdeed or as an insurmountable crisis. "Problems form an important part of our lives," said Elder Horacio A. Tenorio. "They are placed in our path for us to overcome them, not to be overcome by them. We must master them, not let them master us. Every time we overcome a challenge, we grow in experience, in self-assuredness, and in faith."[9]

The impact of attitude and perception is profound. Harvard University professor Douglas Powell tells "a story about two sons of an alcoholic. One turned out to be a drunk, the other a tee-totaler. When asked to explain themselves, each gave exactly the same reply: 'With a father like that, what can you expect?' The moral of the story, it seems to me, is that it's not the problems we have in our lives, but how we manage them that makes so much difference."[10]

As stated, stress involves change. It doesn't always have to be negative change. Stress can be caused by marital conflict or unemployment or serious personal injury, but it can also result from landing a new job, buying a new house, sending a child on a mission, or welcoming a new baby into the family. When the stress of change occurs, the body is forced to adapt to the change. What happens in the body is aptly called the *general adaptation response.* It affects almost all body systems. It was first discovered, and named, by stress pioneer Hans Selye in 1936; scientists now know that the complicated series of physical responses to stress involves more than fourteen hundred known chemical reactions.

The very process of living involves change, so everyone will experience some stress. But when stress is chronic the body must constantly adapt. That's when stress becomes a threat to health, because so much of the body's energy is channeled into coping with stress.[11]

Some stress is caused by what experts call "major life events," such as the death of a spouse or close friend, marital separation or divorce, a change in financial status, or personal injury. But research shows that sometimes the minor hassles can build up and cause problems, such as running out of gas on the way to work, being asked to teach a Church lesson at the last minute, having unexpected company drop in, or getting delayed at a busy intersection. As one behavioral scientist put it, "Sometimes it is not the mountain in front of you, but the grain of sand in your shoe that brings you to your knees."[12]

Regardless of the source of stress, the body's response to stress—the "stress response"—is part of the physical programming that accompanied our creation. It served early humans well: when facing threats in the environment, their bodies reacted in a very specific way that either prepared them to fight for their lives or run for their lives. Appropriately, then, it's also called the "fight-or-flight" response.

What worked so well for early humans, though, isn't usually appropriate for the stresses we face today. Stress is the enemy, and our body's responses are the weapons. But, as one writer put it:

> The problem is that many of our battleship's weapons are beautifully designed, but for the wrong war. The enemy has greatly changed. Our stress responses were programmed for life in the primitive state, thousands of years before we became "civilized." No longer are our stresses a simple matter of life and death threats; they now involve much more intricate and complex challenges.[13]

The stress response involves three major stages:

- *Alarm reaction.* In the first stage, the body immediately responds to stress; a host of physical changes occur that allow the body to combat stress. The immune system is depressed, and the victim becomes more susceptible to infection and disease. If the stress is brief, the body recovers quickly.
- *Resistance.* If stress continues, the body changes to adapt to the prolonged stress. The immune response bounces back and is actually stronger than normal. If this stage could last forever, there would be no problem, but that's not how it works.
- *Exhaustion.* The body eventually loses the ability to keep up with the demands stress puts on it, and it enters the third stage: exhaustion. Simply stated, the body has its limits. They are different in every person, but when the body reaches its limit, it collapses. Immunity breaks down. Organs stop func-

tioning well. Life-preserving reactions are shut down. The result is *diseases of adaptation:* the diseases we know to be stress-related.

The brain is no discriminator when it comes to stress. It reacts the same whether the stress is physical (you are almost hit by a car as you step off the curb), emotional (three of the Young Women at camp want to leave after an argument), or even immune-related (you are confronted by a threatening infection). Take a look at what happens during the stress response, and why it can hurt us:

THE ADRENAL GLANDS. The adrenal glands start pumping out a group of hormones that help the body use energy. In moderation, that's fine. But too much over a prolonged time destroys the body's resistance to cancer, infections, and illness. The body's immune response gets weak; lymph glands shrivel, bones become brittle, blood pressure soars, and the stomach loses its resistance to gastric acid.

THE THYROID GLAND. Under stress, the thyroid pumps out hormones that help us burn fuel faster and give us energy. The result is insomnia, shaky nerves, and exhaustion. It's the reason why some people lose weight under stress.

THE BRAIN. Confronted with stress, the brain releases endorphins (natural pain-killers as potent as some narcotic drugs). When stress is chronic, the body's supply of endorphins is depleted. Then people under stress start suffering from things like migraine headaches, backaches, and even arthritis pain.

SEX HORMONES. Stress reduces testosterone in men and progesterone in women. That was important in early times: decreased fertility came in handy in times of drought, overcrowding, and decreased food supply. Today, unrelenting stress can result in infertility or sexual dysfunction.

DIGESTION. During stress, all the blood is diverted away from the digestive tract and to the muscles, giving the body strength. But eating under stress can cause stomach bloating, nausea, cramping, and diarrhea. Stress can also cause a dry mouth. Dry mouth is such a reliable symptom of stress, in fact, that in China it's used as a lie-detector test.

BLOOD SUGAR. Stress causes a burst of sugar (glucose) to be released into the bloodstream followed by a burst of insulin, which enables the body's cells to use the sugar for energy. That provides "fuel for the sprint." It can also aggravate either hypoglycemia (low blood sugar) or diabetes.

CHOLESTEROL. Stress causes the liver to release cholesterol into the bloodstream where, unfortunately, it's deposited in the blood vessels. The result, of course, leads to heart disease.

THE HEART. The heart starts racing under stress, pumping more blood to the muscles and lungs, enabling fuel and oxygen to be carried more efficiently to the muscles. In fact, blood flow to the muscles of the arms and legs increases three to four hundred percent under stress. Early humans needed it to fight or flee. Today, chronic stress causes high blood pressure.

THE BLOOD. The blood gets thick and clots more easily. That helped early humans fight infection, stop bleeding from a wound, and increase the capacity of the blood to carry oxygen to the muscles. When the blood turns thick under stress today, the result can be heart attack, stroke, or embolus.

THE SKIN. Stress causes the skin to "crawl," blanch, and sweat. Look at what that did for early humans: all of the hairs stood on end, making them look bigger. It gave them a sort of "radar" that helped them detect what was going on in the environment. It heightened their sense of touch, cooled their overheated muscles, and diverted blood away from their wounds. Today, it makes skin less resistant to electricity, the principle behind most lie detector tests.

THE SENSES. Under stress, all five senses are sharper. In early humans, the pupils dilated to enhance night vision; thinking was sharpened; hearing and touch were improved; and the entire body was brought to peak function. The same thing happens today, but chronic stress puts the senses on constant "red alert." Sensory burnout can result. In other words, sight, hearing, taste, smell, and sense of touch can actually become less efficient over time.

All together, these responses combine in a real assault on the body. "We live in a world of uncertainties," summed up cardiologist Herbert Benson, "everything from the nuclear threat to job insecurity to the near assassination of the President to the lacing of medicines with poisons."[14] Stressors like those, say the experts, can build up enough to cause chronic stress, and if the body isn't resilient enough, the final product is illness or disease.

Scientific research has provided countless examples of the diseases linked to stress. One study at Albert Einstein College of Medicine found that children with cancer had twice as many recent crises as similar children who did not have cancer.[15] A study of eight thousand patients with various kinds of cancer concluded that for most, "the cancer appeared during a period of severe and intense life stress often involving loss, separation, and other bereavements."[16] The leading theory is that stress may contribute to cancer because it alters the immune system, giving cancer a chance to develop.[17] And while there is no direct evidence that stress *causes* cancer, some studies indicate that stress may be a factor in the *development* of cancer.

Stress has also been directly linked to the development of all kinds of heart disease. Researchers have noted that in areas of the world where stress is uncommon, heart disease is also uncommon.[18] Interestingly, research has shown that among heart disease patients, mental stress is as dangerous to the heart as is physical stress.[19] In a study conducted at the UCLA School of Medicine among people who had been diagnosed with heart disease, asking patients to discuss their own shortcomings caused almost the same intensity of heart reactions as did the strenuous riding of a stationary bicycle.

A variety of studies have shown that stress can cause sudden cardiac death. In one study, researchers examined a hundred cases of sudden cardiac death drawn from a coroner's records. They discovered that almost two-thirds of the victims were under moderate to severe stress during the final day of life. More than one in five were experiencing severe stress during the last thirty minutes of life. The coroner's reports revealed stressors such as receipt of divorce papers, a fight over a game, an automobile accident, and an attack by dogs as some examples.[20] The sudden deaths were probably due to an irregular heart rhythm and increased nervous input to the heart, both caused by stress.

At particular risk are people known as *hot reactors*, people whose blood pressure seems normal at rest but shoots up to dangerously high levels during stress. Prominent cardiologist Robert S. Eliot says that hot reactors "burn a dollar's worth of energy for a dime's worth of trouble." And, he says, they "are pressure cookers without safety valves, literally stewing in their own juices." Worst of all, "these people do not suspect that their bodies are paying a high price for overreacting to stress."[21]

Stress suppresses the immune system's ability to produce and maintain lymphocytes (the white blood cells that kill infection) and natural killer cells (the specialized cells that seek out and destroy foreign invaders).[22] As a result, stressful incidents can lower resistance to disease.[23]

Left unchecked, constant stress can shorten life. Researchers studied more than 600 people over a period of twelve years. They tested each one at the beginning to determine how much stress each suffered. They found that the existence of distress at the study's beginning was a good predictor of who would die during the study.[24]

The decades of research that have focused on the human stress response and its associated ills pose a fascinating question: Why do some people who have chronic stress fall ill, while others sail through unscathed? The gospel gives us some perspective, as does science. As cited earlier, researcher Suzanne Ouellette Kobasa, who teaches psychology at the City University of New York's graduate school, identified a set of personality traits she called *hardiness*—"a set of beliefs about oneself, the world, and how they interact. It takes shape as a sense of personal commitment to what you are doing, a sense of control over your life, and a feeling of challenge."[25] Kobasa defines the personality traits of hardiness as "the three Cs":[26] commitment, control, and challenge. Added to Kobasa's three Cs is *coherence*, a dynamic feeling that things are basically predictable and the high expectation that all things will work out well.

We have the plan of salvation to make sense of our existence. We know upon whom we can trust. "Perhaps no promise in life is more reassuring than that promise of divine assistance and spiritual guidance in times of need," said President Howard W. Hunter. "It is a gift freely given from heaven, a gift that we need from our earliest youth through the very latest days of our lives."[27]

As Elder Neal A. Maxwell assured us:

> When in situations of stress we wonder if there is any more in us to give. We can be comforted to know that God, who knows our capacity perfectly, placed us here to succeed. No one was foreordained to fail or to be wicked. Let us remember that we were measured before and were found equal to our tasks; therefore, let us continue, but with a more determined discipleship. When we feel overwhelmed, let us recall the assurance that God will not over-program us; he will not press upon us more than we can bear.[28]

In discussing people who were able to overcome stress and disease, *Psychology Today* editor Marc Barasch said that if "there is a thread that stands out, it is that each person, some readily, some reluctantly, wound up doing the opposite of what sick people are supposed to: Rather than only trying to 'get back to normal,' they embarked on a voyage of self-discovery. Like early circumnavigators, they seemed to cling to an instinctive faith that the only way home was forward, into the round but unknown world of the self."[29]

Viktor Frankl, who survived the incomprehensible stress of a Nazi concentration camp, pointed out that no matter how terrible the conditions of psychic and physical stress, man can preserve "the last of the human freedoms—to choose one's attitude in any given set of circumstances, to choose one's own way." Frankl writes:

> Even though conditions such as lack of sleep, insufficient food and various mental stresses may suggest that the

> inmates were bound to react in certain ways, in the final analysis it becomes clear that the sort of person the prisoner became was the result of an inner decision, and not the result of camp influences alone. Fundamentally, therefore, any man can, even under such circumstances, decide what will become of him—mentally and spiritually. . . . It is this spiritual freedom—which cannot be taken away—that makes life meaningful and purposeful. . . . Suffering is an ineradicable part of life, even as fate and death. Without suffering and death human life cannot be complete. The way in which a man accepts his fate and all the suffering it entails, the way in which he takes up his cross, gives him ample opportunity—even under the most difficult circumstances—to add a deeper meaning to his life.[30]

Yale oncologist Bernie Siegel shares the advice he gives cancer patients—advice that plays heavily on the ability to take control and to experience faith and hope:

> If there's one thing I learned from my years of working with cancer patients, it's that there is no such thing as false hope. . . . Hope is real and physiological. It's something I feel perfectly comfortable giving people—no matter what their situation. I know people are alive because I said to them, "You don't have to die."
>
> If statistics say that nine out of ten people die from this disease, many physicians will tell their patients, "The odds are against you. Prepare to die." I tell my patients, "You can be the one who gets well. Let's teach you how."[31]

Kobasa herself says it is possible to develop hardiness, and she recommends two exercises that students of the gospel will easily recognize.

The first is called *compensating through self-improvement.* It's a strategy that helps us overcome stressful situations we can't control by experiencing personal growth in an area we can control. Here's how it works: say the company we work for is purchased by a larger corporation, and our division is abolished as part of the merger. Or say a favorite brother-in-law is killed in a traffic accident. We can't control either of those things, so we compensate. We might learn to pilot a small-engine plane, write the family history we've been researching for a decade, or learn a difficult foreign language that has always interested us. Simply stated, we focus our energies on a new challenge instead of on the stress we can't control. This strategy, says Kobasa, helps us feel confident and in control.

The second strategy is called *reconstructing stressful situations.* In essence, it's a clever way of "rewriting" our own histories—only this time, we come out the winners. Here's how: We start by mentally recalling a stressful event that happened to us; the more stressful, the better, and the more recent, the better. Then we rehearse the whole thing in our mind, and concentrate on remembering as many details as we can. Next we write down three ways the event could have been worse. Finally, we write down three ways it could have been better—in other words, what we could have done to improve the situation. It's the perfect kind of material to record in a journal.

This kind of exercise does three things. First, it helps us realize that things weren't as bad as they could have been, which can help change our perspective on stress. Second, it gives us ideas about what to do better next time—ideas that can help relieve stress about the future. Third, and most important, it gives us a sense of control by teaching that we can influence the way things turn out.

The following exercises can help increase our resilience:

- Learning to welcome the stresses we face as a way of proving our mettle. Brigham Young advised, "The lifetime of man is a day of trial, wherein we may prove to God, in our darkness, in our weakness, and where the enemy reigns, that we are our Father's friends."
- Doing whatever we can to develop creativity, to find new ways of looking at things, or to transform confusion into order. The creative expressions we make through writing, playing a musical instrument, dancing, or painting can also

help us work through stress. Brigham Young advised that "no matter what your circumstances are, whether you are in prosperity or in adversity, you can learn from every person, transaction, and circumstance around you."[32]

- When confronted with a challenge, relying on keen insight. We can ask tough questions; be careful observers; use brainstorming techniques to come up with as many ways as possible to *look at* the situation. And then turn to prayer. President Ezra Taft Benson taught:

> God does hear and answer prayers. I have never doubted that fact. From childhood, at my mother's knee I first learned to pray; as a young man in my teens; as a missionary in foreign lands; as a father; as a Church leader; as a government official. I know without any question that it is possible for men and women to reach out in humility and prayer and tap that Unseen Power; to have prayers answered. Man does not stand alone, or, at least, he need not stand alone. Prayer will open doors; prayer will remove barriers; prayer will ease pressures; prayer will give inner peace and comfort during times of strain and stress and difficulty.[33]

President Spencer W. Kimball advised, "Prayer provides solace. The Lord has not promised us freedom from adversity and affliction. Instead, he has given us the avenue of communication known as prayer, whereby we might humble ourselves and seek his help and divine guidance."[34]

- If we start to feel stressed, we can break our problems down into smaller "chunks" that we can more easily face. We can then take on the easiest challenges first; this will help us gain confidence, and the next problem will be easier to face.
- We can change our perspective on problems: Instead of seeing them as negatives, we should try finding the positives—the exciting challenges that can result. An upcoming professional exam is an undisputed stress, but we can look at studying for

it as a chance to hone skills, increase knowledge, and gain an edge over competitors in the job market. Elder Dallin H. Oaks pointed out the importance of changing perspective:

> Persons who are deprived of sight, hearing, or movement, parents who care for a handicapped child, and persons who are compelled to endure conditions of economic hardship, political oppression, or even obnoxious personal associations, can achieve extraordinary spiritual growth through the process of coping with such adversities. God is just. He knows all things, and all things are present before his eyes (see D&C 38:2). When we can see our own condition and behavior as he sees them, we will understand why he told the imprisoned and suffering Prophet Joseph Smith, "all these things shall give thee experience, and shall be for thy good." (D&C 122:7)[35]

The Prophet Joseph Smith himself traced "increased feelings of sensitivity" to his experience in Liberty Jail. He wrote that "my heart will always be more tender after this than ever it was before. . . . For my part I think I never could have felt as I now do if I had not suffered the wrongs that I have suffered. All things shall work together for good to them that love God."[36]

- We can build our network of social support by enriching family relationships, cultivating a circle of friends. We can stay involved with the people around us by attending church regularly, starting a study group, getting involved in community service, or volunteering at our child's school. Through it all we can develop a sense of humor, as well as a sense of compassion and empathy.

Developing resilience means developing a sense of control, a knowledge that *you* are ultimately the one in charge of what happens to you. One of the best tips comes from psychiatrist Steven Wolin and developmental psychologist Sybil Wolin: "Get revenge by living well instead of squandering your energy by blaming and faultfinding."[37]

One of the best ways to protect yourself from the effects of stress is to face the stress head-on. Recognize it and get ready to deal with it. "Avoiding and denying that stress exists won't make it go away," says Baylor College of Medicine psychologist Michael Cox. "Look at different ways you can change the situation to lessen the stress, make your decision, and face the stress head on. Action is the fastest way to reduce the level of stress."[38]

As Bishop Robert L. Simpson taught, "almost anyone can exceed and excel on calm waters or going down hill when everything is fine. But when you can find the man or woman who can do it when all closes in around him, then you have a winner. . . . Learn how to do things under stress. . . . That is the only difference, really, between someone who succeeds and fails."[39]

Making overall good health choices can also help reduce the effects of stress. Regular exercise, relaxation, a balanced diet, plenty of sleep, and avoidance of harmful substances—in essence, following the Word of Wisdom—increases resistance to disease and illness, even during periods of stress.[40]

Another way to manage the potentially harmful effects of stress is to be realistic with ourselves. Perhaps Elder Boyd K. Packer said it best: "Things we cannot solve, we must survive."[41]

"The stress most faithful Church members feel arises out of the shared pressures of daily life, the temptations and afflictions common to mortals," writes Elder Neal A. Maxwell. "These real pressures are unnecessarily increased when some unwisely place upon themselves unrealistic expectations."[42] In answer to this "avoidable stress," Elder Maxwell points out that the Lord's instructions are very clear:

"Do not run faster than you have strength and means provided to enable you . . . but be diligent unto the end" (D&C 10:4).

Further, the Lord advised, "And see that all these things are done in wisdom and order; for it is not requisite that a man should run faster than he has strength. And again, it is expedient that he should be diligent, that thereby he might win the prize; therefore, all things must be done in order" (Mosiah 4:27).

Elder Maxwell concluded:

> Paced progress not only is acceptable to the Lord but also is recommended by him. Just as divine disclosure usually occurs line upon line, precept upon precept, here a little and there a little, so likewise we will achieve our spiritual progress gradually (see D&C 128:21; 98:12).
>
> Rather as seeing ourselves as failing simply because we do not become immediately perfect . . . an improving person can actually know that the course of his life is generally acceptable to the Lord despite there being much distance yet to be covered.[43]

As faithful members of the Church, there are many other things we can do to better cope with stress and many things we can do to relieve stress. Elder Neal A. Maxwell advises:

> We can ease the stress induced by our inconsistency, pain through which we put ourselves repeatedly. Unfortunately, like Oliver Cowdery, we do not always "continue as [we] commenced" (D&C 9:5). As with our wasteful automobile driving habits that consume extra energy because of quick starts and stops, so it may be that with inconsistent discipleship we actually inflict costs on ourselves in the face of divine counsel. . . .
>
> The enthusiasm of "I'll baptize a thousand on my mission!" is best tempered by "I'll go where you want me to go, dear Lord . . . I'll do what you want me to do," letting "God give the increase" (*Hymns*, no. 270; 1 Corinthians 3:6).
>
> We can be overwrought by seeking the praise and honors of the world. Such individuals are "anxiously engaged" in putting points on a local scoreboard. Heavy stress occurs in gaining the whole world while losing our souls (see Mark 8:36). . . .
>
> We can likewise diminish (at least our portion of) the painful stress that accompanies unresolved interpersonal differences: "Moreover if thy brother shall trespass against thee, go and tell him his fault between thee and him alone:

> if he shall hear thee, thou hast gained thy brother" (Matthew 18:15).
>
> We can end the exhausting stress that goes with jealousies and fears (see D&C 67:10).
>
> We can end the subtle but awful stress of resisting conscience (see Mosiah 4:3).
>
> We can dissolve the stress of wearily listening to "so many kinds of voices in the world" (1 Corinthians 14:10). A true disciple need tune in on only one channel: "My sheep hear my voice" (John 10:27). . . .
>
> So it is that we can end much stress in life, if we will. Genuine discipleship is a way of shedding the sources of stress.[44]

One of the greatest sources of stress is sin we have not repented of. "When sins are committed, emotional stress is the result," warned Elder Alvin R. Dyer. "There is only one way to get a release from it—and this is through repentance."[45] True repentance, true forsaking of sin, brings "peace of mind, a form of regeneration, that enables one to go on in life in pursuit of true happiness."[46]

As Elder Neal A. Maxwell advised, we can end the "genuine stress which goes with unrepented-of sin" by pleading, "More holiness give me," and by receiving the "peace . . . which passeth all understanding."[47]

We have within our grasp the knowledge, the power to overcome the ravages of stress, to rise amid affliction, to persevere. The Lord's promises are reassuring:

"Great tribulations shall be among the children of men, but my people will persevere" (Moses 7:61).

As we are promised, "peace be unto thy soul; thine adversity and thine afflictions shall be but a small moment;

"And then, if thou endure it well, God shall exalt thee on high; thou shalt triumph over all thy foes" (D&C 121:7-8).

As Elder Russell M. Nelson told us, "With celestial insight, trials impossible to change become possible to endure."[48]

END NOTES

1. H. Burke Peterson, "Adversity and Prayer," *Ensign,* January 1974, p. 19.
2. B.H. Roberts, *The Gospel and Man's Relationship to Deity* (Salt Lake City: Deseret Book, 1965), p. 278.
3. Ibid.
4. Neal A. Maxwell, *Notwithstanding My Weakness* (Salt Lake City, Utah: Deseret Book, 1981), pp. 20-21.
5. David O. McKay, *Conference Report,* October 1936, p. 103.
6. Neal A. Maxwell, *All These Things Shall Give Thee Experience* (Salt Lake City: Deseret Book, 1980), pp. 26-27.
7. Bernie S. Siegel, *Love, Medicine, and Miracles* (New York: Harper and Row, 1986), p. 71.
8. Leonard A. Sagan, *The Health of Nations* (New York: Basic Books, Inc., 1987), p. 82.
9. Horacio A. Tenorio, "Teachings of a Loving Father, *Ensign,* May 1990, p. 79.
10. Speech at the Eighth Annual Conference on Health and Wellness, Brigham Young University, Provo, Utah,1988.
11. Paul Pearsall, *Super Immunity* (New York: McGraw-Hill, 1987).
12. Ian Wickramasekera, "Risk Factors Leading to Chronic Stress-Related Symptoms," *Advances* 4(1): 1987, p. 21.
13. Peter G. Hanson, *The Joy of Stress* (Kansas City, Mo.: Andrews, McMeel, and Parker, 1986), p. 29.
14. Claudia Wallis, "Stress: Can We Cope?" *Time,* June 6, 1983, pp. 48-54.
15. Bernie S. Siegel, *Love, Medicine, and Miracles* (New York: Harper and Row Publishers, 1986), p. 72.
16. H.J.F. Baltrush, reported at the Third International Symposium on Detection and Prevention of Cancer.
17. Guy R. Newell, "Stress and Cancer," *Primary Care and Cancer,* May 1991, p. 30.
18. Andrew G. Goliszek, *Breaking the Stress Habit* (Winston-Salem, N.C.: Carolina Press, 1987), p. 84.
19. C. Noel Bairey et al., "Mental Stress as an Acute Trigger of Left Ventricular Dysfunction and Blood Pressure Elevation in Coronary Patients," *American Journal of Cardiology* 66, 1991, p. 28G.

20. Peter Riech, "How Much Does Stress Contribute to Cardiovascular Disease?" *Journal of Cardiovascular Medicine,* July 1983, pp. 825-31.
21. Robert S. Eliot and Dennis L. Breo, "Are You a Hot Reactor? Is It Worth Dying For?" *Executive Health* 20(10), 1984, pp. 1-4.
22. Andrew G. Goliszek, *Breaking the Stress Habit* (Winston-Salem, N.C.: Carolina Press, 1987), 85.
23. "Can Undue Stress Lower Resistance to Disease?" *Medical Times,* April 1988, pp. 99-100.
24. P.D. Somervell, B.H. Kaplan, and G. Heiss, "Psychologic Distress as a Predictor of Mortality," *American Journal of Epidemiology,* 130(5): 1989, pp. 1013-1023.
25. Joshua Fischman, "Getting Tough," *Psychology Today,* December 1987, pp. 26-28.
26. Joan Borysenko, *Minding the Body, Mending the Mind* (Reading, Mass.: Addison-Wesley, 1987), p. 24.
27. Howard W. Hunter, "Blessed from On High," *Ensign*, November 1988, p. 59.
28. Neal A. Maxwell, *Brigham Young University Speeches of the Year* (Provo, Utah: BYU Press, 1978), p. 156.
29. Proceedings of the Sixth International Conference of the National Institute for the Clinical Application of Behavioral Medicine (1994), *The Psychology of Health, Immunity, and Disease,* Volume B, p. 9.
30. Viktor L. Frankl, *Man's Search for Meaning,* revised edition (Beacon Press, 1962), pp. 104-105.
31. Bernie Siegel, "Mind Over Cancer," *Prevention,* March 1988, pp. 61-62.
32. John A. Widtsoe, compiler, *Discourses of Brigham Young* (Salt Lake City, Utah: Deseret Book, 1978), p. 250.
33. Ezra Taft Benson, *Teachings of Ezra Taft Benson* (Salt Lake City, Utah: Bookcraft, 1988), p. 434.
34. Spencer W. Kimball, *The Teachings of Spencer W. Kimball,* comp. by Edward L. Kimball (Salt Lake City, Utah: Bookcraft, 1982), p. 115.
35. Dallin H. Oaks, *Pure in Heart* (Salt Lake City, Utah: Bookcraft, 1988), p. 67.
36. Neal A. Maxwell, *But For a Small Moment* (Salt Lake City, Utah: Bookcraft, 1986), p. 111.

37. Susan Chollar, "The Miracle of Resilience," *American Health,* April 1994, p. 75.
38. "Learn to Manage the Stress in Your Life," *Healthline,* September 1993, p. 6.
39. Robert L. Simpson, *BYU Speeches,* April 20, 1965, p. 8.
40. T. Edward Hannah, "Hardiness and Health Behavior: The Role of Health Concern as a Moderator Variable," *Behavioral Medicine,* Summer 1988, pp. 59-62.
41. Boyd K. Packer, *Conference Report,* October 1987, p. 20.
42. Neal A. Maxwell, *Men and Women of Christ* (Salt Lake City: Bookcraft, 1991), p. 22.
43. Ibid., p. 23.
44. Neal A. Maxwell, *Men and Women of Christ* (Salt Lake City: Bookcraft, 1991), pp. 25-26.
45. Alvin R. Dyer, *Conference Report,* April 1964, p. 77.
46. Alvin R. Dyer, *Conference Report,* October 1969, p. 56.
47. Neal A. Maxwell, *Men and Women of Christ* (Salt Lake City: Bookcraft, 1991), pp. 25-26.
48. Russell M. Nelson, "With God Nothing Shall Be Impossible," *Ensign,* May 1988, p. 35.

Adversity itself may lead toward and not away from God and spiritual enlightenment; and privation may prove a source of strength if we can but keep a sweetness of mind and spirit.

— David O. McKay

Perhaps it is best to step back from the trees in order to see the forest. A trait is a "tree" which clearly has individual significance, but all the trees form a forest or pattern in the personality.

— NEAL A. MAXWELL

CHAPTER

10

The Disease-Prone Personality

Giant strides in the battle against disease have been made during the last half-century. Children once paid a terrible price for diseases like measles, mumps, and rubella; today, immunizations protect against these and others. Diseases that were common just a few generations ago—polio, smallpox, diphtheria, tetanus—are scarcely known today. We've even conquered most bacteria: strep throat, which killed President George Washington, can now be cured with a simple ten-day course of antibiotics.

But we haven't done so well with many other diseases; maladies such as heart disease and cancer, for example, are leading killers. And recent research shows that instead of relying solely on medications for a cure, we must look to ourselves—to the way we think, the way we behave, the way we react to stress, the way we express anger. Because research shows that in large part, personality—the consistent core of character and temperament that dictates how we react to the world around us—may play a major role in disease.

Howard S. Friedman, a psychologist and clinical professor of community medicine at the University of California, wrote, "I have never seen a death certificate marked 'Death due to unhealthy personality.' But maybe pathologists and coroners should be instructed to take into account the latest scientific findings on the role of personality in health."[1]

Whether they know it or not, most people associate certain personality types with particular diseases. Workaholics have heart attacks. Worriers get ulcers. People who are too uptight have asthma. In reality, can things be so neatly categorized?

Not yet. But researchers have shown that personality impacts health. They know that the way we look at things, as determined by our personality, may either keep us well (as we discussed in Chapter 3) or may actually contribute to illness.

The notion of a disease-prone personality may be disturbing to some; at first, it may seem to contradict the notion of divine origin or seem too general. But it is important to look at the research, some of which is compelling. We are not maintaining that our Father in Heaven endowed us with character traits that would certainly bring us illness and misery. But our premortal experiences and choices may have caused some to have traits—hostility, pessimism, despair—that could possibly lead to disease.

The most complete early studies on the link between personality and disease were pioneered by Yugoslav psychologist Ronald Grossarth-Maticek, who began his studies in his native country and eventually involved people in Germany. At the time, no one had done research on people who were healthy at the beginning of the study, but that's exactly what Grossarth-Maticek did.[2] Based on their personalities, he predicted which patients would be likely to develop cancer, to develop heart disease, or to stay healthy. Thirteen years later, he checked on the people. The results were remarkable: he was able to predict death from cancer based on personality with *six times greater accuracy* than predictions based on cigarette smoking. His predictions about heart disease and maintaining good health were equally impressive. Even though his studies were conducted as early as the 1960s, their results are consistent with those of studies conducted as recently as last year.

In trying to determine how personality influences health, researchers have looked at the impact of personality on the immune system, the body system most directly linked to health. In one study, a team of psychiatrists and psychologists at Charles River Hospital in Massachusetts studied more than a hundred Harvard University students who were physically healthy. They then took blood samples, exposed the blood to cancer cells, and measured how many tumor cells were destroyed during a four-hour period. All the students, regardless of personality traits, had some immunity against cancer. But the more unhealthy the personality, the fewer cancer cells were killed; these were the students who were unhappy, socially withdrawn, pessimistic, and guilt-ridden, and who had low self-esteem. Blood from students with the healthiest personalities—those who could adapt to various situations—killed *forty times more cancer cells* than the others.[3]

One of the most widely studied personalities is what researchers call the "coronary-prone personality," or simply, the collection of traits that seems to increase the risk of heart disease. They call it the *Type A behavior pattern.* Cardiologists Ray Rosenman and Meyer Friedman originated a theory three decades ago that a major risk factor for heart disease was a behavior pattern characterized by the rush to achieve increasingly more in less time. With their research, "Type A personality" became a household phrase.

At first, the two described Type A as "hurry sickness." In fact, for several decades, scientists concentrated on some of the more obvious characteristics of the Type A behavior pattern: hurried behavior and mannerisms, a sense of time urgency, the need to do more than one thing at a time, competitiveness, insecurity, and aggression. Friedman, in fact, described the epitome of a man with hurry sickness: he used two electric shavers so he could shave both sides of his face at the same time. Another researcher described a man who liquefied his food in a blender so he wouldn't have to waste time chewing. And still another described a man who saved time spent going to the bathroom by keeping a bottle at his desk.[4]

What scientists eventually discovered is that, while the "hurry-sickness" aspects of Type A personality are the best known, they are also probably the least harmful to health. A second generation of very sophisticated studies identified the "toxic core" of Type A behavior, the set of traits that creates the greatest risk to health. The "toxic core" is the exact opposite of the prescription Christ gave us when he said, "Therefore, what manner of men ought ye to be? Verily I say unto you, even as I am" (3 Nephi 27:27). We are, the Savior taught us, to be slow to anger. We are to be kind and forgiving and lose ourselves in the service of others, banishing absorption with self.

As it turns out, time urgency isn't the problem. The biggest threats to health for a Type A personality are hostility, anger, cynicism, suspiciousness, and excessive self-involvement. The most dangerous of the toxic core traits is what scientists call *free-floating hostility*, a permanent, deep-seated anger that hovers quietly until some trivial incident triggers an explosion. Because this hostility is chronic, even minor irritations can bring on a rage. People with free-floating hostility react with seething anger; they dwell on the objects of their despising. Many are physically abusive. This kind of anger is not the kind of righteous indignation the Savior demonstrated as he cleared the money-changers from the temple. It's an anger that is always there, waiting to latch onto something, no matter how illogical. A driver explodes if the car in front of him does not pull out of the intersection quickly enough. A shopper becomes loudly profane if forced to wait in line. Someone launches into an abusive tirade when a teenaged girl with a loud radio walks by.

An important part of free-floating hostility is the cynical mistrust of other people's motives. According to Williams, they think other people are not to be trusted—that other people will lie and cheat if they can get away with it. The kind of personality at highest risk, says Williams, is "deeply suspicious. They feel that they must remain constantly on guard against others, whom they believe are dishonest, antisocial, and immoral." Some believe you can have many of the characteristics typically associated with

Type A without running the risks of a heart attack *as long as you are not hostile.*

Renowned experts like Williams point to hostility as one of the most crucial factors in heart disease. "We have strong evidence that hostility alone damages the heart," Williams emphasizes. In one study, hostility was shown to increase the risk of heart disease by a staggering *seven times.*

The other traits in the toxic core are also damaging to the heart. Anger sends blood pressure skyrocketing and provokes the body to create unhealthy chemicals; combined with hostility, Williams says, "anger is poison."[5] People who are suspicious are constantly "on guard," which increases the level of harmful stress hormones in their blood. Added to that is a cynical mistrust of others, which, according to Williams, starts a chain reaction:

> Expecting that others will mistreat us, we are on the lookout for their bad behavior—and we can usually find it. This generates frequent anger to which the hostile person is prone, and that anger, combined with a lack of empathy for others—a natural consequence of the poor opinion we hold of others in general—leads us to express our hostility overtly, in the form of aggressive acts towards others.[6]

There's a reason why the toxic core traits cause health problems. Psychologist Paul Pearsall gives a vivid description:

> The supersystem sizzles with neurochemical changes, we roast in our hormonal stew, and, as if by some universal wisdom, the body can be stopped in its tracks by adopting an "enough is enough" strategy. We overload, our heads start pounding for attention, our hearts get attacked for our lack of intimacy, and our vessels cause the doctor's mercury gauge to warn us that things are getting too high. Even our bowels can get irritated with us and show their displeasure in their own unique language. Somewhere in our bodies, . . . something is burning out.[7]

Type A behavior is basically an exaggerated stress response. Responding to what it believes is a threat, it starts pumping out stress hormones, which cause physical damage. The body is on constant alert; it never relaxes. The body—and especially the cardiac system—pays the price. The overload of stress hormones causes increased levels of cholesterol and other fats in the blood; the blood gets thicker and is prone to clotting; and damage occurs to the heart and arteries. Blood pressure skyrockets. Too much insulin is produced, interfering with the body's ability to use fats and sugars and damaging the blood vessels. Magnesium is leached from the cells and eliminated through the urine, which can disrupt the heart's rhythm and cause sudden death. And, finally, the stress hormones affect the immune system, interfering with the body's ability to fight infection.

A second area of considerable research—and controversy—is the possibility of a "cancer-prone personality," a set of personality traits that increases the risk of cancer. Researchers first became keenly interested in that possibility during the 1950s, when psychologist Eugene Blumberg began noticing a "trademark" personality among cancer patients in a Long Beach veterans' hospital. He wrote, "We were impressed by the polite, apologetic, almost painful acquiescence of the patients with rapidly progressing disease as contrasted with the more expressive and sometimes bizarre personalities of those who responded brilliantly to therapy with remissions and long survival."[8]

Following several studies, Blumberg concluded that the patients with the fastest-growing tumors were the ones who were "consistently serious, overcooperative, overly nice, overly anxious, painfully sensitive, passive, and apologetic." Those with the slowest-growing tumors were the ones who had developed good ways of coping with life's stresses.

Subsequent research showed that cancer patients were often nice—*too nice.* University of California School of Medicine psychologist Lydia Temoshok eventually identified what she called the Type C personality—in essence, the opposite of the hard-driving Type A personality. She maintained that the Type C patients were overwhelmed by emotions they had been unable to express or resolve. She determined that behavior and personality may not *cause* cancer, but certain personality traits may affect how a person copes with stress and may at least influence the outcome of the disease. She went so far as to say that people with a Type C personality are likely to have "a worse outcome than might be expected on medical grounds."[9]

Temoshok says the hallmark of the cancer personality is the "nonexpression of emotion,"[10] and other researchers agree. Many cancer patients have unresolved tension that they refuse to express or resolve. While cancer patients are often described by other people as kind, sweet, and benign, this sweetness is "really a mask they wear to conceal their feelings of anger, hurt, and hostility."[11]

One of the most prominent cancer-personality researchers is psychologist Lawrence LeShan. He found that not only did cancer victims tend to have similar personalities, but there was a striking similarity in their life histories. He found three specific "life events" that seemed common to cancer patients:

- Cancer patients described a "bleak" childhood, had a tense and hostile relationship with one or both parents, and felt lonely and isolated. They thought it was impossible to have a "safe," satisfying relationship with another person.
- As young adults, they finally made a strong emotional commitment—to a person, a job, a cause, a religion, or something else. The object of the emotional investment became the centerpiece of their lives.
- Something happened to take away the object of emotional investment: the spouse died. They got fired. A beloved child forsook the family. There was nothing to replace the great void, and six to eight months later, they were diagnosed with cancer.[12]

It's important to note that in this, as in almost all other areas of medical research, there are inconsistencies in research findings.[13] And, with those inconsistencies, we need to be cautious about any findings. Speaking to the fourth national conference on the Psychology of Health, Immunity, and Disease, Henry Dreher said:

> People do not give themselves cancer. Patients who believe that, by dint of their personality, behavior, or inadequacy, or some kind of death wish, they have brought cancer upon themselves should be disabused of this idea. Cancer can result from an immunological breakdown caused, only in part, by psychological factors operating below the level of consciousness.[14]

Regardless of where you stand on the controversy over personality and health, there's one clear fact: we all respond differently to the stresses and problems that confront us in life. Whether it's a bad day or a chronic emotional crisis, some sail through valiantly, and others get sick. Part of the reason is physiological. Part falls back onto personality.

As Latter-day Saints, we know it is within our power to make the changes that will bring us greater satisfaction and joy. President Ezra Taft Benson, referring to the mighty change described in the scriptures (see Alma 5:26), said:

> The Lord works from the inside out. The world works from the outside in. The world would take people out of the slums. Christ takes the slums out of the people, and then they take themselves out of the slums. The world would mold men by changing their environment. Christ changes men, who then change their environment. The world would shape human behavior, but Christ can change human nature.[15]

We know, too, that stress and adversity are an important part of the experience we have on this earth. This knowledge, when fully appreciated and coupled with our brief glimpses into eternity, may make us more able to cope with the stress that occurs. Added to that unique perspective is that of the plan of salvation. We understand that this life is but one step in a glorious progression—not the first, and certainly not the last. We know that we will live forever, and that our personalities will be perpetuated everlastingly.

As we look for balance of personality that will ultimately bring health, Elder Bruce R. McConkie reminds us of the possibility inherent in personality:

> All men are spirit children of God the Eternal Father. In the premortal life we all dwelt in his presence, saw his face, and heard his voice. We were as well acquainted with him in that day as we are with our earthly fathers in this. The spirit within us is the offspring of God. Now housed in a tabernacle of clay, it is the intelligent, sentient, believing, knowing part of the human personality.[16]

END NOTES

1. Howard S. Friedman, *The Self-Healing Personality* (New York: Henry Holt and Company, 1991), p. 1.

2. Hans J. Eysenck, "Personality, Stress, and Cancer: Prediction and Prophylaxis," Part I, *British Journal of Medical Psychology,* Vol. 61, 1988, pp. 57-75.

3. Bruce Bower, "Personality Linked to Immunity," *Science News,* Vol. 130, 1986, p. 310.

4. Jeffrey Pepper Rodgers, "Type A: Healing the Spirit," *Psychology Today,* April 1989, p. 262.

5. Earl Ubell, "The Deadly Emotions," *Parade,* February 11, 1990, pp. 4-6.

6. Redford Williams, "The Trusting Heart," *New Age Journal,* May/June 1989, p. 26.

7. Paul Pearsall, *Super Immunity* (New York: McGraw-Hill, 1987), p. 52.

8. Steven Locke and Douglas Colligan, *The Healer Within: The New Medicine of Mind and Body* (New York: E. P. Dutton, 1986), p. 140.

9. Ibid., pp. 133-34.

10. Ibid., p. 134.

11. Michael A. Weiner, *Maximum Immunity* (Boston: Houghton-Mifflin Company, 1986), p. 179.

12. Steven Locke and Douglas Colligan, *The Healer Within: The New Medicine of Mind and Body* (New York: E.P. Dutton, 1986), pp. 133-34.
13. Howard S. Friedman, *The Self-Healing Personality* (New York: Henry Holt and Company, 1991), p. 62.
14. Henry Dreher, "The Type C Connection: A Powerful New Tool in the Fight Against Cancer," in Proceedings of the Fourth National Conference on the Psychology of Health, Immunity, and Disease, published by the National Institute for the Clinical Application of Behavioral Medicine, Boston, Mass., 1992.
15. Ezra Taft Benson, "Born of God," *Ensign*, November 1985, p. 6.
16. Bruce R. McConkie, *A New Witness for the Articles of Faith* (Salt Lake City: Deseret Book, 1985), p. 45.

Instead of relying solely on medications for a cure, we must look to ourselves—to the way we think, the way we behave, the way we react to stress, the way we express anger.

— The Authors

You can know the difference between the Spirit of the Lord and the spirit of the adversary, when you find that you are happy and contented, that you love your fellows, that you are anxious for their welfare; and you can tell that you do not have that spirit when you are full of animosity and feel that you would like to knock somebody down.

— HEBER J. GRANT

CHAPTER

11

ANGER, HOSTILITY, AND HEALTH

The Book of Mormon provides one of the most convincing examples of the pervasive power of hostility. The classic discord between the Nephites and the Lamanites far exceeded mere irritation or casual dislike. To understand it, we need to consider how it began: after leaving Jerusalem, Lehi's family found itself in a strange land. The wilderness was harsh. Their small band was continually threatened with destruction.

Throughout their experience, three of the brothers reacted in distinctly different ways. Laman and Lemuel were, we are told, "slow to remember the Lord" (1 Nephi 17:45). They dissented. They "began to murmur exceedingly, because of their sufferings and afflictions in the wilderness" (1 Nephi 16:20). Though they had been visited by an angel—and though the angel spoke to them in a voice of thunder—they were "past feeling" and failed to be touched (1 Nephi 17:45).

Nephi, on the other hand, remained faithful. As he describes it, he looked unto God, "and I did praise him all the day long; and I did not murmur against the Lord because of mine afflictions" (1 Nephi 18:16). Because he stayed faithful and followed the commandments, he was "favored of the Lord" (Mosiah 10:13). In fact, though he was not the oldest, the Lord appointed him leader over his brothers—an event Laman and Lemuel reacted to with anger, saying, "We will not that our younger brother shall be a ruler over us" (1 Nephi 18:10).

The struggle between the three persisted. Occasionally Laman and Lemuel were humbled, but mostly they seethed with rebellion and hostility. On more than a few occasions they tried to murder Nephi. In Lehi's final blessing to his two sons, he pleaded with them:

> Awake, my sons; put on the armor of righteousness. Shake off the chains with which ye are bound, and come forth out of obscurity, and arise from the dust.
>
> Rebel no more against your brother, whose views have been glorious, and who hath kept the commandments from the time that we left Jerusalem; and who hath been an instrument in the hands of God, in bringing us forth to the land of promise; for were it not for him, we must have perished with hunger in the wilderness; nevertheless, ye sought to take away his life; yea, and he hath suffered much sorrow because of you.
>
> And I exceedingly fear and tremble because of you, lest he shall suffer again; for behold, ye have accused him that he sought power and authority over you; but I know that he hath not sought for power nor authority over you, but he hath sought the glory of God, and your own eternal welfare. (2 Nephi 1:23-25)

Still the contention persisted. In fact, the hostility Laman and Lemuel felt toward Nephi was conveyed to their children, and their children's children, and beyond. The Lamanites, we are told, became "a wild, and ferocious, and a blood-thirsty people, believing in the tradition of the iniquities of their fathers" (Mosiah 10:12). Consider what Laman and Lemuel passed on to their children: "And thus they have taught their children that they should hate them, and that they should murder them, and that they should rob and plunder them, and do all they could to destroy them; therefore they have an eternal hatred towards the children of Nephi" (Mosiah 10:17).

"The result of this sad circumstance," wrote Elder Neal A. Maxwell, "reflects not only historical hostility, but 'eternal hatred' as well. . . . Today's world trembles because of ancient grievances and hatreds." In fact, he emphasized, "seldom does one encounter, especially so succinctly, the awful manner in which hatred can be instilled, generation after generation, in a whole people who were conditioned to feel they had been wronged again and again."[1]

Hostility and anger have become so common that many accept them as normal—even inevitable, or necessary. We are clearly instructed by the Savior: "He that hath the spirit of contention is not of me, but is of the devil, who is the father of contention, and he stirreth up the hearts of men to contend with anger, one with another" (3 Nephi 11:29). According to Elder Marvin J. Ashton, what begins with contention can bind us to heavier sins that can "destroy our eternal lives. A contentious spirit can affect almost any phase of our lives."[2]

During his brief mission in mortality the Savior decried the *attitudes* of hatred and hostility more than he condemned the acts those attitudes prompt. For, as he set it forth, the gospel of Jesus Christ "is a gospel of love and kindness. It will cause us, if we are living as we should, to love our neighbors as ourselves."[3]

"Let all bitterness, and wrath, and anger, and clamour, and evil speaking be put away from you," wrote the Apostle Paul to the Ephesians (Ephesians 4:31-32). It was but one of several warnings about anger Paul included in his epistle. In a separate letter to the Galatians, Paul referred to wrath—anger—as one of the works of the flesh (see Galatians 5:19-20). Finally, he asked, "Can ye be angry, and not sin?" (Ephesians 4:26; Joseph Smith Translation).

Everyone has felt anger, a temporary emotion that provokes both the body and the emotions. It can range all the way from cool resentment to intense rage. It may or may not be expressed outwardly through verbal insults, profanity, or physical gestures (such as slamming a door). Anger, which is temporary, is not the same as *hostility*, which is a permanent attitude caused by an ongoing accumulation of anger.

Anger changes the way we look at others and the way we look at ourselves. Anger can cause us to break commitments and covenants. Anger can keep us from praying. Anger can even lead us away from truth. As Lucifer departed in anger, wrote Elder Neal A. Maxwell, so will others "depart in anger. [And] Like Lucifer, they will take all they can with them."[4]

Added to the grave spiritual consequences of anger are serious *physical* consequences. The exploding rage you feel when you get really angry brings with it actual physical changes in your body, such as the release of hormones and chemicals that affect many organs and systems.

"Anger kills," says famed Duke University researcher Redford Williams. "We're speaking here not about the anger that drives people to shoot, stab, or otherwise wreak havoc on their fellow humans. We mean instead the everyday sort of anger, annoyance, and irritation that courses through the minds and bodies of many perfectly normal people."[5]

The words we use to describe our anger strongly hint at the turmoil that goes on inside our bodies when we're angry. Social psychologist and anger expert Carol Tavris reminds us of some of the most common: "You make my *blood boil.*" "He was *bursting with anger.*" "I *blew my stack.*" "She *flipped her lid.*"[6]

When we are seized with anger, the last thing we may stop to consider is the effect of anger on the body. Tongue in cheek, Frederick Buechner describes it like this:

> Of the seven deadly sins, anger is possibly the most fun. To lick your wounds, to smack your lips over grievances long past, to roll over your tongue the prospect of bitter confrontations still to come, to savor to the last toothsome morsel both the pain you are given and the pain you are giving back—in many ways it is a feast fit for a king. The chief drawback is that what you are wolfing down is yourself. The skeleton at the feast is you.

According to medical research, "no matter how many times you work out at the gym or how careful you are to eat correctly, you're putting yourself at risk if you don't manage your anger effectively."[7] To appreciate the broad impact of anger, look at the wide range of physical reactions that go along with it:[8] muscle tension, scowling, grinding of teeth, glaring, clenching of fists, redness of the face, goosebumps, chills and shudders, prickly sensations, numbness, choking, twitching, sweating, losing self-control, or feeling hot or cold. Blood rushes to the face, the heart speeds up, breathing gets faster, blood pressure rises, digestion slows down, and the muscles tense up.

One of the major effects of anger is the release of chemicals and hormones associated with stress; if there's enough anger, say the researchers, almost any part of the body can be damaged. One of the most devastating effects of anger is on the heart and the circulatory system. The hormones released during anger affect the ability of both large and small arteries to narrow or widen. That, says famed cardiac researcher Meyer Friedman, is "chiefly responsible for the development of arterial diseases."[9] Research published in the *New England Journal of Medicine* concluded that mismanaged anger might even be the principal factor in predicting heart disease.

Prolonged or chronic anger also leads to high blood pressure. In a study at the University of Michigan School of Public Health, men with the lowest blood pressure were the ones who kept their cool; they acknowledged their anger, but were not openly hostile. The ones with the highest blood pressure were the ones who either bottled up their anger or became openly hostile.[10]

Recent research gives important information as to why anger causes heart disease. Research reported to the American Psychosomatic Society shows that people who seethe with anger and try to repress it are slowest at getting rid of dietary fat. Anger might also affect the heart muscle itself by actually decreasing the heart's pumping ability.[11]

There may also be a link between anger and cancer, a connection that was implicated in studies done as long as four decades ago. More recent research has shown that the style of expressing anger (or the ability to express it at all) seems to have considerable impact on both the development and spread of cancer. In a study of women with breast disease, those who were later diagnosed with cancer had an entirely different anger style: they were much more likely to suppress their anger and then finally explode when they could no longer hold it in. Many didn't express anger at all.[12] A number of other studies have shown a possible link between suppression of anger and cancer. In one study, patients who suppressed anger had fewer immune cells fighting at the tumor sites. When these patients were taught how to express anger appropriately, immune system activity improved.

It's not realistic to think you'll never get angry; even the Savior became angry on occasion. The way you *express* anger has a lot to do with how healthy you are. University of Arizona psychologist Roger J. Daldrup points out two classic methods of expressing anger in an unhealthy way: misdirecting it or suppressing it completely.[13] Misdirected anger "is the classic kicking the cat because you're angry at your spouse maneuver. Though people seem to be expressing it, they are just burying the real problem and creating more problems along the way." Complete suppression of anger doesn't work, either, because it works like the soft pedal on the piano to dull all the emotions.

Other unhealthy ways of expressing anger include miscommunication, becoming emotionally distant, escalating the conflict, endlessly rehearsing grievances, assuming a hostile disposition, acquiring angry habits, making a bad situation worse, losing self-esteem, and acting in such a way as to lose the respect of others.[14]

What is needed, researchers agree, is the ability to confront the source of anger and express feelings without getting overwhelmed by the anger. As Tavris put it, "The purpose of anger is to make a grievance known, and if the grievance is not confronted, it will not matter whether anger is kept in, let out, or wrapped in ribbons and dropped in the Erie Canal."[15]

Healthy expression of anger requires that you face the situation early, before it has a chance to accumulate and fester. Anger that is properly expressed is finished—and it's processed out of the system. With that comes the ultimate blessing. As Daldrup writes:

> [Properly expressing anger] is liberating, not destructive. Don't be afraid. You won't get stuck in your rage. You won't put your relationship at risk. You will, however, free up the energy you were using to stuff your anger down. That's more energy for enjoying sunsets, listening to music, appreciating our children, our relationships, study, exciting work, helping others, spiritual growth, travel, making love. The options are endless, and they are ours. This is freedom.[16]

Even more lethal than anger is *hostility;* hostility comes from the Latin word *hostis,* which means *enemy.* For the hostile, enemies seem to abound. They are everywhere: at the office, in the elevator, in the grocery store checkout line, on the freeway, next door, in the ward. Ironically, because of what hostility does to health, hostile people also become their own enemy.

When we are hostile, we "spew forth hatred and animosity" toward the people with whom we associate; that attitude, wrote Elder Bruce R. McConkie, leads to desolation in this life and "everlasting destruction" in the next life.[17] Indeed, said President Spencer W. Kimball, the bitterness of hostility is poison: it "injures the one who carries it; it hardens and shrivels and cankers."[18] Bitterness, he said, poisons the mind and kills the spirit.

In a very real way, the bitterness of hostility may also kill the body. Hostility is an ongoing accumulation of anger and irritation; it is a permanent kind of anger that is expressed with greater frequency and in response to increasingly trivial things.[19] Hostile people become threatening and aggressive; they are cynical of others. Redford Williams, whose research on hostility is making medical history, says that hostility "is a basic lack of trust in human nature, in human motives. It's a belief that people are more bad than good, and that they will mistreat you."[20]

It may be easier to understand the concept of hostility if you have a clear picture of the opposite state of mind: the trusting heart. According to Williams,

> [The] trusting heart believes in the basic goodness of humankind, that most people will be fair and kind in relationships with others. Having such beliefs, the trusting heart is slow to anger. Not seeking out evil in others, not expecting the worst of them, the trusting heart expects mainly good from others and, more often than not, finds it. As a result, the trusting heart spends little time feeling resentful, irritable, and angry. From this it follows that the trusting heart treats others well, with consideration and kindness; the trusting heart almost never wishes or visits harm upon others.[21]

Hundreds of studies over the past two decades by psychologists and scientists specializing in the immune and nervous systems show beyond doubt that attitudes and emotions have a significant impact on health, and the emotions related to hostility have the most pronounced impact of all. There are two main reasons why: first, hostility causes a constant release of stress hormones that work to destroy health in a variety of ways. Second, hostility weakens the part of the nervous system that is designed to calm the body down after an emergency or an episode of emotional stress.

The combination of hormones released with hostility:

- Significantly increase the risk of heart attack. In fact, the hormones released during hostility can make the coronary arteries spasm, resulting in heart attack.[22]
- Cause early development of arteriosclerosis (narrowing and hardening of the arteries), which greatly increases the risk of heart disease. *Even when they're not angry,* hostile people produce hormones that cause an outpouring of fats that boost the risk of heart disease.[23]
- Weaken the immune system; in one study, the hormones completely prevented immune cells called macrophages from killing tumor cells.

- Interfere with the body's DNA repair system, knocking out the first line of defense against a number of diseases, including cancer.
- Shut off the "thermostats" in the walls of the blood vessels that bring blood pressure back to normal.
- Block sugar from entering the brain's cells, interfering with their proper function.

Because of its effects on the immune system, hostility has been definitely linked to poor physical health in general, and especially to heart disease. The factors cited above—higher blood pressure, early arteriosclerosis, spasms of the coronary arteries, and elevated blood fats (including cholesterol)—all explain why hostility causes heart disease. As Redford Williams describes it, "Hostile men get angry more often and with greater intensity than others, and each and every time, it hits the heart."

Hostility has been shown to cause coronary heart disease, coronary blockage, and coronary death. It has also been shown to significantly increase the risk of a second heart attack and to lead to premature death of people with existing heart disease. In fact, hostility contributes to premature death from many causes. In one study, students in a law school were followed for twenty-five years. Only 4 percent of the non-hostile lawyers died from any cause, but 20 percent of the hostile attorneys died during the same period.[24]

Duke University psychologist John Barefoot and his colleagues followed five hundred middle-aged people for fifteen years; all had similar health and lifestyle patterns. Those who had scored high on hostility tests had more than six times the death rate of those with low scores. When the researchers compiled death records at the end of the study, about one-fifth of the participants had died; the survivors were generally the ones with low hostility and less suspiciousness.[25]

Hostility is hazardous—hazardous to outlook, hazardous to health, hazardous to life, and hazardous to the spirit. But Redford Williams and others who have pioneered studies on hostility believe that hostile people can change. Williams and others suggest trying the following techniques to reduce levels of hostility:

- Admitting to someone that we are too hostile and that we are trying to do something about it. Just admitting it makes us more accountable to ourselves.
- Monitoring cynical thoughts, and when we find ourselves becoming cynical, yelling, "Stop!"
- Having a silent conversation in which we reason with ourselves. If we can't distract ourselves from anger, we can try to talk ourselves out of anger. Or we can figure out alternative ways of approaching the situation.
- Meditating when we find ourselves getting hostile. We can learn effective ways to relax, and practice them when we feel anger or hostility starting to build.
- Trying to become more empathetic to the plight of others.
- Increasing our social connectedness; cultivating friends at church, at work, and in the neighborhood. Forgiving people when they wrong us. Learning to trust; listening; getting a pet.
- Trying some of Diane Ulmer's recommended drills:[26] Practicing smiling at others, complimenting others, giving ourselves permission to stay calm when things don't go the way we want, laughing at ourselves, playing fun games, not using obscenities, and looking for opportunities to say, "Maybe I'm wrong."
- Volunteering to help people who are less fortunate.
- Learning more about the teachings of the Church and making a genuine effort to follow the Savior's teachings and example.
- Pretending that today is your last day.

The Savior's example prescribes that we become pure in heart, that we disallow selfishness, and that we make no room for hatred and hostility. It requires that we put away cynicism, and abolish anger and contention. It decrees that we follow the scriptural admonition: "Let all bitterness, and wrath, and anger, and clamour, and evil speaking be put away from you, with all malice: And be ye kind one to another, tenderhearted, forgiving one another, even as God for Christ's sake hath forgiven you" (Ephesians 4:31-32).

Can we as mortals become like the Savior, even surrounded by the world in which we live? One of the best examples for us was the Apostle Paul. As President Spencer W. Kimball wrote:

> Paul was willing to leave the judgment and penalty to the Lord, who would be wise and just. In spite of all he suffered at the hands of oppressors, some of whom were his own false brethren, he was not consumed and scorched with hate or bitterness or rancor. Quite the reverse.
>
> To the Corinthians he urged the very traits he had so fully developed in himself (2 Corinthians 11:23-28). Here we have the noble Paul who had suffered much from his contemporaries: Paul, who had been tortured with beatings, who had suffered incarceration in many prisons; Paul, who had received two hundred stripes across his back, who had been beaten with rods; Paul, who had been stoned and left for dead, and who had three times been shipwrecked and had struggled many hours in the water; Paul, who had suffered from robbers and had been hidden from his pursuers and had escaped in a basket over the wall. This Paul, who had suffered so much at the hands of others came near the end of his life with a forgiving heart and said: "At my first answer no man stood with me, but all men forsook me: I pray God that it may not be laid to their charge." (2 Timothy 4:16.)[27]

As President David O. McKay wrote, the greatest need of the world today "is peace. The turbulent storms of hate, of enmity, of distrust, and of sin are threatening to wreck humanity. It is time for men—true men—to dedicate their lives to God, and to cry with the spirit and power of the Christ, 'Peace, be still. . . . ' (Mark 4:39.)"[28]

END NOTES

1. Neal A. Maxwell, *Plain and Precious Things* (Salt Lake City: Deseret Book, 1983), pp. 72-73.
2. Marvin J. Ashton, *Conference Report,* April 1978, p. 12.
3. George Albert Smith, *Conference Report,* October 1948, pp. 167-68.

4. Neal A. Maxwell, *Things As They Really Are* (Salt Lake City: Deseret, 1980), Introduction.
5. Redford Williams and Virginia Williams, *Anger Kills* (New York: Random House/Times Books, 1993), p. xiii.
6. Carol Tavris, "On the Wisdom of Counting to Ten," in P. Shaver, ed., *Review of Personality and Social Psychology* 5 (Sage, 1984), pp. 173-74.
7. Hendrie Weisinger, "Mad? How to Work Out Your Anger," *Shape,* January 1988, pp. 86-93.
8. Carol Tavris, *Anger: The Misunderstood Emotion* (New York: Touchstone, 1982).
9. Barbara Powell, *Good Relationships Are Good Medicine* (Emmaus, Penn.: Rodale Press, 1987), pp. 158-59.
10. Emrika Padus, *The Complete Guide to Your Health and Your Emotions* (Emmaus, Penn.: Rodale Press, 1986), p. 496.
11. "Depression, Anger, and the Heart," *Harvard Health Letter,* February 1993, p. 7.
12. Emrika Padus, *The Complete Guide to Your Health and Your Emotions* (Emmaus, Penn.: Rodale Press, 1986), p. 498.
13. Roger Daldrup, "How a Good Dose of Anger Therapy Can Restore Peace of Mind," *Your Personal Best,* April 1989, p. 8.
14. Carol Tavris, "On the Wisdom of Counting to Ten," in P. Shaver, ed., *Review of Personality and Social Psychology,* 5 (Sage, 1984), pp. 170-91.
15. Ibid., p. 191.
16. Roger Daldrup, "How a Good Dose of Anger Therapy Can Restore Peace of Mind," *Your Personal Best,* April 1989, p. 8.
17. Bruce R. McConkie, *A New Witness for the Articles of Faith* (Salt Lake City: Deseret Book, 1985), p. 377.
18. Spencer W. Kimball, *The Teachings of Spencer W. Kimball,* comp. by Edward L. Kimball (Salt Lake City: Bookcraft, 1982), p. 103.
19. Robert Ornstein and David Sobel, *The Healing Brain* (New York: Simon and Schuster, 1987), p. 181.
20. Emrika Padus, *The Complete Guide to Your Emotions and Your Health* (Emmaus, Penn.: Rodale Press, 1986), p. 595.
21. Redford Williams, *The Trusting Heart: Great News About Type A Behavior* (New York: Times Books Division of Random House, Inc., 1989), p. 71.

22. J. L. Marx, "Coronary Artery Spasms and Heart Disease," *Science* 208, pp. 1127-30, and E. Braunwald, "Coronary Artery Spasm," *Journal of the American Medical Association,* Vol. 244, No. 17, pp. 1957-59.
23. "How Hostile Thinking Makes You Heart-Sick," *Your Personal Best,* April 1989, p. 5.
24. Kathy A. Fackelmann, "Hostility Boosts Risk of Heart Trouble," *Science News,* Vol. 135, 1989, p. 60.
25. The Editors of *Prevention* magazine and the Center for Positive Living, *Positive Living and Health: The Complete Guide to Brain/Body Healing and Mental Empowerment* (Emmaus, Penn.: Rodale Press, 1990), p. 155.
26. Diane K. Ulmer, "Helping the Coronary Patient Reduce Hostility and Hurry Sickness: A Structured Behavioral Group Approach," *The Psychology of Health, Immunity, and Disease,* Vol. A, p. 592, in Proceedings of the Sixth International Conference of the National Institute for the Clinical Application of Behavioral Medicine, Hilton Head S.C., 1994.
27. Spencer W. Kimball, *The Miracle of Forgiveness* (Salt Lake City: Bookcraft, 1969), pp. 278-79.
28. David O. McKay, *Gospel Ideals,* comp. by G. Homer Durham (Salt Lake City: The Improvement Era, 1953), p. 295.

Despair is the enemy of our souls. It can paralyze us, halt our progress, and cause us to lose our way. . . . We can endure all things when our hope is centered in the one who will never fail us—our Savior, Jesus Christ, who is the light of the world.

— DWAN J. YOUNG

CHAPTER

12

Depression, Despair, and Health

"We live in an age when, as the Lord foretold, men's hearts are failing them, not only physically but in spirit (see D&C 45:26)," President Ezra Taft Benson told Saints in a message most timely for our day. "Many are giving up heart for the battle of life. Suicide ranks as a major cause of death among college students. As the showdown between good and evil approaches, with its accompanying trials and tribulations, Satan is increasingly striving to overcome the Saints with despair, discouragement, despondency, and depression."[1]

Despair, wrote Elder Neal A. Maxwell, "is an acquired reflex, but once acquired it is like a dandelion: it needs so little soil or encouragement to sprout afresh." Elder Bruce R. McConkie defined despair as "a feeling of hopelessness and futility, a feeling that there is no chance for continued progression or forgiveness, or salvation." The spirit of the Lord brings cheerfulness and hope, he wrote, but "the spirit of the devil casts men into despair and despondency."[2]

In fact, Elder Marvin J. Ashton said, one of Satan's "most powerful tools" is discouragement. His counsel was simple yet powerful: "Don't let your discouragement make Satan rejoice."[3]

Closely related to despair is depression, but neither is the same as grief. Dr. Michael Irwin of the University of California at San Diego points out that people who are depressed always feel down, blue, and gloomy. People who are grieving move in and out of those feelings.

Depression, too, is much more than an occasional sad mood. Life is a series of natural ups and downs, and everyone who lives occasionally feels sadness and grief. After all, the Lord said that "My people must be tried in all things, that they may be prepared to receive the glory that I have for them" (D&C 136:31). Elder Robert E. Wells explained with clarity that mortality is purposely riddled with experiences that can bring despair:

> One of the purposes of this life is to be tested, tried, and proven to see how well we will serve the Lord. The Prophet Joseph said that we would be tested to see if we would serve and remain faithful through all hazards. We knew before we came that there would be many adverse circumstances to test us: accidents, sickness, and disease to prove us; temptations and distractions to try us; disappointments, discouragements, reverses, failures, and all kinds of situations to determine our character.[4]

Our challenge is to look with a sense of hope beyond those intermittent periods of sadness, "to refuse to let the bad things that *happen* to us do bad things *to* us. That is the crucial difference between adversity and tragedy."[5] As Harry Emerson Fosdick wrote, "a healthy person believes in the validity of his high hours even when he is having a low one." Or, as the scriptures promise, "thine adversity and thine afflictions shall be but a small moment" (D&C 121:7).

A person who is depressed, on the other hand, believes he can't tolerate either the present conditions or the future possibilities. He simply quits. He gives up. A depressed person "goes on strike" from life, doing less and less, losing interest in people, abandoning hobbies, giving up at work,[6] and sometimes even giving up on the gospel or the Savior. Prayers often cease. Shrouded in despair inspired by Satan, who would "destroy our glory and remove our crown,"[7] a person who is depressed loses eternal perspective. He loses sight of himself as a child of God. He doubts his worth—and his worthiness.

Depression and despair strike without respect for status or rank. Well-known people throughout history have struggled with the "black dog of depression"—Abraham Lincoln, Ernest Hemingway, Winston Churchill, Sylvia Plath, Thomas Eagleton, and even Biblical figures, including Saul and Nebuchadnezzar.[8] Depression is often associated with illness, disability, isolation, bereavement, and poverty.[9]

Depression is twice as common among women, possibly because, as one expert claims, women think about problems in ways that amplify depression.[10] Depression may also result from what has been humorously called "the Mormon super-mom syndrome": a set of self-inflicted expectations that leave a woman feeling less than worthy if she can't study the scriptures, bake bread, run five miles, and sew a child's school play costume before the rest of her family wakes up in the morning.

Depression is more common among people with poor social support or a lack of supportive relationships. It tends to run in families. And it can lead to self-destruction: some experts estimate that as many as 15 percent of those who are depressed eventually commit suicide.[11]

Like the common cold, depression can cause a variety of symptoms that range from mild to severe. Those symptoms are not imagined; rather, they arise from a very real physical upset in the body. Frederick Goodwin, scientific director of the National Institute of Mental Health, says that depression is the richest, most striking example in psychiatry—and possibly in all of medicine—of the relationship between the mind and the body.[12]

Depression causes changes in the body similar to those caused by stress; one of its most significant effects is on the immune system. Depression causes the adrenal gland to secrete far too much cortisol, which then suppresses the immune system.[13] Then, because depressed people have no apparent "biological brake" to turn off cortisol production, the immune system progressively slows down. Physicians have long noted that depressed people complain about getting "everything that's going around," a truth that naturally follows suppressed immunity.

Depression actually has several specific effects on the immune system. To begin with, research shows that it reduces the activity of natural killer cells, the "surveillance" cells that seek out and destroy viruses and tumor cells. It also reduces the number of white blood cells, which fight bacteria and other foreign invaders. Other tests show that depression affects the relationship between cells that turn on and off the immune response.

A number of impressive studies have also shown that depression causes heart rate, blood pressure, and coronary artery function to go amiss, leading to heart attack and heart disease. The effect of depression on the heart is so profound that researchers have been able to predict who would have a heart attack based solely on depression. Perhaps some of the most profound effects of depression hit people who already have heart disease; a study conducted at the Washington University School of Medicine in St. Louis[14] found that major depression was the best single predictor of which heart patients would have serious problems and complications—a better predictor, in fact, than factors like age, cigarette smoking, cholesterol levels, or even how damaged the arteries were. Almost eighty percent of the depressed people in the study had some cardiac event during the twelve months after diagnosis; only a third of the non-depressed patients had problems.

Still another study done in a Canadian hospital found that people who are seriously depressed immediately following a heart attack have a greater than average chance of dying, regardless of their physical condition. All else being equal, depression raised the risk of death 3.4 times and the risk of having another heart attack by 5.7 times.[15]

Aside from specific medical conditions, the hopelessness, frustration, sadness, and dissatisfaction that constitute depression can quite literally make you feel bad physically. In many studies, the greater the depression, the higher the number of physical symptoms associated with any illness.[16] An estimated one-fourth of all patients who see primary-care physicians are depressed; more than one-tenth are suffering from major depression; and an estimated three-fourths of all depressed people see physicians because they are physically ill.[17]

Depression itself can be a potent risk factor in determining whether a person will die sooner than expected, whether of "natural causes" or of disease. In one study of nursing homes in the Baltimore area, depression at the time of admission raised the risk of death within a year by fifty-eight percent, *regardless of physical health.*[18] In another study of two thousand men employed by Chicago's Western Electric Company, men who were most depressed at the beginning of the study were most likely to die within twenty years, even when researchers considered traditional risk factors, such as age, occupation, cigarette smoking, and family history.[19]

Recent experiments at the National Institute of Mental Health have identified one of the most significant factors in depression: sunlight. They've classified a specific type of depression called *seasonal affective disorder* (SAD), a condition that causes lethargy, anxiety, and depression as winter approaches and the days grow shorter and darker.[20] Researchers have found that light therapy—exposure to strong artificial, broad-spectrum white light for thirty to sixty minutes a day—can significantly reduce or even eliminate the symptoms of depression and distress for SAD victims.[21]

Scientists who are continuing research into the disorder believe the retina of the eye may transmit light to a particularly sensitive area of the brain; they emphasize that *looking at* the light, not just being exposed to it, may provide the greatest benefits. There is, of course, a possible spiritual explanation as well: during periods of apostasy, we are told, darkness figuratively covered the earth. During the three days following the Savior's crucifixion, the earth was smothered by an oppressive darkness. But the light of Christ "is the light by which the worlds are controlled, by which they are made. It is the light of the sun and all other bodies. It is the light which gives life to vegetation. It quickens the understanding of men."[22]

There are many other ways to help ease depression. Depending on individual circumstances, medical science offers medication, behavioral science offers therapy, and rest and exercise have been advocated. In addition to those, as President Ezra Taft Benson reminded us, "the Lord has provided ways which, if followed, will lift our spirits and send us on our way rejoicing."[23]

What are those ways? The first is to follow the commandments of God. Elder Neal A. Maxwell wrote, "When iniquity increases, so do despair and alienation. . . . No wonder we despair when we sin, because we act against our own interests and against who we really are. When we are imprisoned by iniquity, we turn the cell lock ourselves."[24] President Ezra Taft Benson said that "those who ignore God's holy laws will always live in despair."[25]

For those who have slipped, there is hope. "For those who pay the price required by true repentance, the promise is sure," wrote President Benson. "You can be clean again. Despair can be lifted. The sweet peace of forgiveness will flow into your lives."[26]

Examples throughout the scriptures elegantly illustrate that the Atonement can reach even those in the deepest despair. Remember, the Lord is waiting for us. As Elder Neal A. Maxwell so eloquently put it, "there are no restrictive office hours for receiving returning prodigals—night and day He awaits us!"[27]

Overcoming obstacles and staying on the path can be difficult; it may, in fact, be an exercise of sheer endurance. Christian, the main character in the masterful *Pilgrim's Progress,* struggled toward the celestial city in a powerful display of endurance. One of his greatest obstacles was the Giant Despair—an obstacle that sometimes requires the determined grit of endurance. In essence, said President Benson, "there are times when you simply have to righteously hang on and outlast the devil until his depressive spirit leaves you."[28] To maintain perspective and endurance requires not only unflinching faith, but faithful prayer.

As Isaiah prophesied, the Lord was sent "to bind up the brokenhearted" (Isaiah 61:1); there is no burden too great for Him, no depression he cannot lift. "People who search for a light at the end of the tunnel other than the light of Jesus Christ will not find it," wrote Elder Neal A. Maxwell. "Knowing, however, that His light is eternal, steadfast, unwavering, and constant can see us through the narrowest passages."[29] President Ezra Taft Benson taught:

> To press on in noble endeavors, even while surrounded by a cloud of depression, will eventually bring you out on top into the sunshine. . . . While you are going through your trials, you can recall your past victories and count the blessings that you do have with a sure hope of greater ones to follow if you are faithful. And you can have that certain knowledge that in due time God will wipe away all tears (Revelation 7:17) and that "eye hath not seen, nor ear heard, neither have entered into the heart of man, the things which God hath prepared for them that love him." (1 Corinthians 2:9.)[30]

END NOTES

1. Ezra Taft Benson, *Conference Report*, October 1974, p. 65.
2. Bruce R. McConkie, *Mormon Doctrine,* 2nd edition, revised (Salt Lake City: Bookcraft, 1966), p. 191.
3. Marvin J. Ashton, *Conference Report*, April 1984.
4. Robert E. Wells, "How Well Can You Fly It When Everything Goes Wrong?" *New Era,* June 1978, p. 5.
5. "Viewpoint: Antidotes to Adversity," *Church News,* December 8, 1985, p. 16.
6. Bernie S. Siegel, *Love, Medicine, and Miracles* (New York: Harper and Row, 1986), p. 78.
7. Marvin J. Ashton, *Conference Report*, April 1984.
8. Anne H. Rosenfeld, "Depression: Dispelling Despair," *Psychology Today,* June 1985, p. 28.

9. G. J. Kennedy, H. R. Kelman, C. Thomas, W. Wisniewski, H. Metz, and P. E. Bijur, "Hierarchy of Characteristics Associated with Depressive Symptoms in an Urban Elderly Sample," *American Journal of Psychiatry,* Vol. 146, No. 2, 1989, pp. 220-25.
10. Martin E. P. Seligman, *Learned Optimism* (New York: Alfred A. Knopf, 1991), p. 75.
11. Anne H. Rosenfeld, "Depression: Dispelling Despair," *Psychology Today,* June 1985, p. 28.
12. Winifred Gallagher, "The Dark Affliction of Mind and Body," *Discover,* May 1986, pp. 66-76.
13. "Depression and Immunity," *Harvard Medical School Mental Health Letter,* 1986, p. 68.
14. R. M. Carney, M.W. Rich, K.E. Freedland, J. Saini, A. TeVelde, C. Simeone, and K. Clark, "Major Depressive Disorder Predicts Cardiac Events in Patients with Coronary Artery Disease," *Psychosomatic Medicine,* 50, 1988, pp. 627-32.
15. Nancy Frasure-Smith, Francois Lesperance, and Mario Talajic, "Depression Following Myocardial Infarction: Impact on Six-Month Survival," *Journal of the American Medical Association,* Vol. 270, 1993, pp. 1819-25.
16. K. Bolla-Wilson and M. L. Bleecker, "Absence of Depression in Elderly Adults," *Journal of Gerontology,* Vol. 44, No. 2, 1989, pp. 53-55.
17. Wayne Katon, "Depression: Somatization and Social Factors," *The Journal of Family Practice,* Vol. 27, No. 6, 1988, pp. 579-80.
18. Barry W. Rovner, Pearl S. German, Larry J. Brant, et al., "Depression and Mortality in Nursing Homes," *Journal of the American Medical Association,* Vol. 265, 1991, pp. 993-96.
19. Howard S. Friedman, *The Self-Healing Personality* (New York: Henry Holt and Company, 1991), p. 61.
20. T. Silverstone and C. Thompson, ed., *Seasonal Affective Disorder* (London: Clinical Neuroscience Publishers, 1989).
21. D.A. Oren and N. E. Rosenthal, "Seasonal Affective Disorders," in E.S. Paykel, ed., *Handbook of Affective Disorders,* 2nd edition (London: Churchill Livingstone, 1992), pp. 551-67; and M. Terman, "On the Question of Mechanism in Phototherapy for Seasonal Affective Disorder: Considerations of the Clinical Efficacy and Epidemiology," *Journal of Biological Rhythms,* Vol. 3, 1988, pp. 155-72.

22. Joseph Fielding Smith, *Doctrines of Salvation,* Vol. 1, p. 52.
23. Ezra Taft Benson, *Conference Report*, October 1974, p. 65.
24. Neal A. Maxwell, *Things As They Really Are* (Salt Lake City: Deseret Book, 1980), p. 8.
25. Ezra Taft Benson, *Teachings of Ezra Taft Benson* (Salt Lake City: Bookcraft, 1988), p. 458.
26. Ibid., p. 284.
27. Neal A. Maxwell, *Men and Women of Christ* (Salt Lake City: Bookcraft, 1991), p. 27.
28. Ezra Taft Benson, *Teachings of Ezra Taft Benson* (Salt Lake City: Bookcraft, 1988), p. 459.
29. Neal A. Maxwell, *Wherefore, Ye Must Press Forward* (Salt Lake City: Deseret Book, 1977), p. 64.
30. Ezra Taft Benson, *Conference Report,* October 1974, p. 65.

Press Forward, Having a Perfect Brightness of Hope

With God's help, good cheer permits us to rise above the depressing present or difficult circumstances. It is a process of positive reassurance and reinforcement. It is sunshine when clouds block the light.

— Marvin J. Ashton

CHAPTER

13

Optimism and Explanatory Style

Elder Orson F. Whitney liked to tell the story of two buckets that hung over a well on either end of a long chain. When one dipped into the dark, cool waters of the well, the other emerged into the dazzling sunlight—and vice versa.

Both were buckets. Both were stationed at the same well. Both were doing the same kind of work. But one bucket was an optimist, and the other was a pessimist.

The pessimistic bucket complained endlessly of its lot. "No matter how full I come up," it whined, "I always go back empty." The optimistic bucket responded with a bright retort: "No matter how empty I go down, I always come up full." For us, as for the buckets, much in life depends on the spirit with which we view it.

As Elder Hartman Rector, Jr., defined it, "The optimist, as you probably know, is a person who, when he wears out his shoes, just figures he's back on his feet."[1]

Modern-day revelation admonishes us to "be of good cheer" (D&C 78:18)—an attitude defined by Elder Marvin J. Ashton as "a state of mind or mood that promotes happiness or joy."[2] That state of mind is a very individual thing and largely determines our outlook.

A wonderful example is told of a mother who brought her twin boys to a psychologist. They were the same in every detail, right down to the last freckle. But, the mother claimed, Roy was an eternal pessimist, and Tom an eternal optimist. She hoped the psychologist could help balance them a little.

"That's easy," said the doctor. "For their shared birthday next week, give the little pessimist a roomful of the best toys in the world. Give the optimist a pile of horse manure." That, he claimed, should do the trick.

The mother reluctantly complied, preparing the boys' rooms as instructed. On the boys' birthday, the parents quietly looked in on Roy the pessimist. There he sat with all the magnificent toys. "What junk!" he said. "There are too many things here to play with. My parents must have something up their sleeves. I hate this stuff. They can't buy me off."

The disappointed parents moved to Tom the optimist's room. There sat Tom, happily digging through the manure. "You can't fool me!" said Tom, looking up at his parents. "Where there's manure, there must be a pony!"[3]

Like Tom the optimist, we can look on the bright side. In a fireside for married couples, President Gordon B. Hinckley quoted a newspaper columnist in saying that "Life is like an old-time rail journey—delays, sidetracks, smoke, dust, cinders, and jolts interspersed only occasionally by beautiful vistas and thrilling bursts of speed. The trick is to thank the Lord for letting you have the ride." But that's not all, President Hinckley admonished us: "The trick, my brethren and sisters, is to enjoy the journey."[4]

As we make our journey, what is our view of life? Elder Neal A. Maxwell points out that our view can be either through the "peephole of pessimism" or through the picture window of awe and wonder. The choice, he says, is up to us. Which offers the better view: the peephole or the picture window? The answer is obvious and compelling. When we choose the picture window, we "will see not only more clearly, but more broadly, the realities, obligations, and opportunities" that surround us.[5]

The way we see things, whether through the peephole or the picture window, is called *explanatory style.* It's the way we perceive the events in our lives. It's the way we explain the bad things that happen to us. In reality, it's a habit; it's a way of thinking that we use when all the factors are equal and there is no clear-cut right or wrong answer. It's more than a mood; it's the way we interpret the good and bad things in life.

When something bad has happened to us, such as losing a job, having a serious falling-out with a friend, or facing financial problems, our explanatory style determines how we perceive the event. If we have a pessimistic explanatory style, we may believe the event happened because of a permanent character flaw that affects everything we do. If we have an optimistic explanatory style, we may believe the event is a one-time, temporary problem resulting from bad luck, circumstances, or another's actions. Explanatory style offers an explanation for the good things, too: the pessimist figures it's a stroke of luck that will never happen again. The optimist believes it's due to effort and skill and can be repeated.[6]

American Institute of Stress President Paul Rosch used an amusement park example to illustrate differences in explanatory style: "Look at how two people might experience a roller-coaster ride. One has his back stiffened, his knuckles are white, his eyes shut, jaws clenched, just waiting for it to be over. The wide-eyed thrill seeker relishes every plunge, can't wait to do it again."[7]

As University of Pennsylvania psychologist Martin Seligman describes it, explanatory style is "a theory about your past, your future, and your place in the world."[8] And once we have formulated a theory, he adds, we tend to find evidence for it in any situation that comes along. Most significant, says Seligman, explanatory style works like a self-fulfilling prophecy: "Those who believe they are the masters of their fate are more likely to succeed than those who attribute events to forces beyond their control."[9]

Research shows that explanatory style has a powerful influence on health and wellness. Yale cancer specialist and surgeon Bernie Siegel says that a pessimistic explanatory style can put a damper on the immune system and stop the healing process. On the other hand, an optimistic explanatory style and the emotions it embraces, such as love, acceptance, and forgiveness, stimulate the immune system and kick the body's own healing systems into gear. Basically, an optimistic explanatory style sends "live" messages to the body and helps promote the healing process.[10]

Robert Good, former president and director of the Memorial Sloan-Kettering Cancer Hospital in New York, maintains that an optimistic explanatory style can actually alter the ability to resist infections, allergies, autoimmune diseases, and even cancer.[11] Michael A. Lerner, a MacArthur Foundation Genius Award winner, agrees: "Attitudes themselves have a very potent effect on the immune system. You become different than the person who developed the cancer. Becoming a different personality may change the environment the cancer grew in; it may become so inhospitable that the cancer shrinks."[12]

Siegel, who works with cancer patients to help them change their explanatory style, says they experience remarkable changes in the course of their cancer as a result. And he claims that explanatory style contributes a great deal to the ability of people to fight cancer. He says that most cancer patients are willing to sit back and let a physician direct the treatment. Some, he says, are happy to die, because "their lives are in shambles." And about one in five have optimistic explanatory styles that make them "truly exceptional survivors."[13]

What about pessimism and optimism themselves? Pessimism affects performance on the job, performance in sports, personal relationships, and the ability to cope. It leads to indecision, anxiety, depression, inertia, and a general feeling of unhappiness. And it also affects health and longevity. In study after study, pessimists consistently have the poorest health.

A pessimistic attitude apparently has tremendous influence on the outcome of disease. Dr. Gerald Jampolsky, who has done extensive research on pessimism, writes:

> [There's] no question that negativity can be incapacitating. If you spend your whole life determining what is impossible, it limits you as to what is possible. If you spend your whole life worrying and feeling guilty, you will never know what it feels like to be truly happy and at peace. And that makes it pretty tough to tap in on our healing energies.[14]

Pessimism has such a powerful influence on health that researchers have been able to use it to predict which people would get sick. One reason is that pessimism affects immunity. In one study of elderly people, the pessimists had significantly impaired immune function and were less able to fight infection and disease.[15] In another study involving almost three hundred men and women, those who were pessimists had the weakest immune systems by far. Researchers who conducted the study said the impaired immune systems of pessimists "might contribute to premature death as well as illness."[16]

Still other research shows that pessimism can actually "turn off" the immune system by depleting a set of chemicals that in turn cause an increase in endorphins. As the level of endorphins increases, the immune system turns itself down.[17] The inevitable result, of course, is that pessimists don't live as long as optimists. Researchers in one study tracked more than six thousand adults in Alameda County, California, for nine years. They found that the men who were pessimistic had two times the risk of dying prematurely; among the women, the risk was a striking five times higher.[18]

On the other hand, a growing body of evidence gives increasing credibility to the idea that optimism promotes health. It has been shown to speed healing and improve results after surgery, even in diseases as grave as cancer. A UCLA team of researchers launched a national survey of cancer specialists in an attempt to find out what psychological factors were most important in helping patients get better. Almost 700 cancer specialists responded to the survey based on their experience with more than 100,000 cancer patients. More than 90 percent said the most significant factor in effective treatment was an attitude of hope and optimism.[19]

Studies at the University of Texas Health Science Center in Dallas reviewed two hundred terminal cancer patients. They found that certain personality traits were common to the patients who lived the longest: They utterly refused to give up. They were open to new ideas. They rejected their role as invalids. They refused to accept the limits of their illness. And, most important, they were optimistic. They believed in themselves and their ability to beat the cancer. One oncologist in Houston utilizes optimism to its fullest: before he ever treats a patient for cancer, he introduces the patient to another who has survived the same condition.

Research has shown that optimists are more successful and perform better than pessimists in almost all fields, including education, business, sports, and politics, partly because they are more resilient under stress. Studies have shown that people who meet stress head-on with a sense of optimism and control don't get sick as often as those who meet stress with pessimism. As one writer so aptly put it, "winners are healthier than whiners."[20]

Researchers suggest the following ways to boost optimism:

- Realizing we need to make a lifestyle change.
- Starting small by choosing one area of life in which to become more optimistic, and then becoming aware of the way we think in relation to that area.
- Taking a good, hard, critical look at our beliefs about ourselves and about that area of life: How realistic are they?
- Setting goals that are small enough to achieve quickly, and then rewarding ourselves when we meet those goals. It's important to reward ourselves when we reach even the most modest goal.
- Seeking out optimistic people and seeking a good friend.
- "Playing" at being optimistic and staying flexible.[21]

And we can try the following ways to raise an optimistic child:[22]

- Being consistent, positive, and responsive, and to the extent that we can, "programming" the child's world to be consistent, positive, and responsive.
- Giving the child responsibility, encouraging independence

and involving the child in a variety of age-appropriate activities.

- Setting realistic goals and encouraging problem solving.
- Teaching the child not to generalize from specific failures but instead, helping the child see failure as a challenge to do better next time.
- Encouraging humor as a way of coping.
- Challenging any pessimistic views the child may express.
- As well as possible, screening the child's peers and teachers for pessimistic tendencies.
- And, finally, being role models of realistic optimism.

Of all people, said President Ezra Taft Benson, "we as Latter-day Saints should be the most optimistic and the least pessimistic. For while we know that 'peace shall be taken from the earth, and the devil shall have power over his own dominion,' we are also assured that 'the Lord shall have power over his saints, and shall reign in their midst.' (D&C 1:35-36.)"[23]

"Our optimism looks to the ultimate outcome, in which right will prevail," wrote Elder Neal A. Maxwell. "The Lord will reign personally on the earth. Truth and justice will be established."[24]

As President Gordon B. Hinckley told the audience at general conference:

> I am a newspaper reader, and I have seen a good deal of this earth. I have seen its rot and smelled its filth. I have been in areas where war rages and hate smolders in the hearts of people. I have seen the appalling poverty that hovers over many lands. I have seen the oppression of those in bondage and the brutality of their overlords. I know something of the misguided youth whose appearance is repugnant, whose hygiene is repulsive, whose manners are disgusting. I have watched with alarm the crumbling morals of our society.
>
> And yet I am an optimist. I have a simple and solemn faith that right will triumph and that truth will prevail. I am not so naive as to believe there will not be setbacks, but I believe that "truth crushed to earth will rise again."

Of course, we will experience setbacks. But as members of the Church, we have special reason to maintain optimism. The reason for our optimism is the gospel itself. For, as the Prophet Joseph Smith proclaimed, "Now, what do we hear in the gospel which we have received? A voice of gladness! A voice of mercy from heaven; and a voice of gladness for the living and the dead; glad tidings of great joy. . . . Let your hearts rejoice, and be exceedingly glad" (D&C 128:19, 22).

And, as Elder Ashton concluded, "With good cheer, carrying our cross can be our ladder to happiness. . . . How powerful and comforting is the Savior's declaration: 'In the world ye shall have tribulation: but be of good cheer; I have overcome the world.' (John 16:33.)"[25]

END NOTES

1. Hartman Rector, Jr., *Conference Report*, April 1979, p. 41.
2. Marvin J. Ashton, *Conference Report*, April 1986, p. 84.
3. From Paul Pearsall, *Super Joy: Learning to Celebrate Everyday Life* (New York: Doubleday, 1988), p. 80.
4. Gordon B. Hinckley, *Cornerstones of a Happy Home*, pamphlet, 1984, p. 4.
5. Neal A. Maxwell, *Behold, I Say Unto You, I Cannot Say the Smallest Part Which I Feel* (Salt Lake City: Deseret Book, 1973), p. 12.
6. Morton Hunt, "Don't Worry, Be Happy," *Longevity*, December 1991, p. 80.
7. "Good Stress: Why You Need It to Stay Young," *Prevention*, April 1986, pp. 28-32.
8. Carolyn Jabs, "New Reasons to Be an Optimist," *Self*, September 1987, pp. 170-73.
9. Martin E. Seligman, *Learned Optimism* (New York: Alfred A. Knopf, 1991), p. 178.
10. "Mind Over Cancer: An Exclusive Interview with Yale Surgeon Dr. Bernie Siegel," *Prevention*, March 1988, pp. 59-64.
11. Blair Justice, "Think Yourself Healthy," *Prevention*, May 1988, pp. 27-32.
12. Daniel Goleman, "The Mind Over the Body," *New Realities*, March/April 1988, pp. 14-19.

13. "Mind Over Cancer: An Exclusive Interview with Yale Surgeon Dr. Bernie Siegel," *Prevention*, March 1988, pp. 59-64.

14. Emrika Padus, *The Complete Guide to Your Emotions and Your Health* (Emmaus, Penn.: Rodale Press, 1986), pp. 519-20.

15. "Longevity: Men Are Catching Up," *Medical World News,* October 12, 1987.

16. Blair Justice, *Who Gets Sick: Thinking and Health* (Houston, Tex.: Peak Press, 1987), p. 231.

17. Martin E.P. Seligman, *Learned Optimism* (New York: Alfred A. Knopf, 1991), pp. 176-78.

18. Blair Justice, "Think Yourself Healthy," *Prevention,* June 1988, pp. 31-32, 105-108.

19. Norman Cousins, *Head First: The Biology of Hope* (New York: E.P Dutton, 1989), p. 217.

20. Sharon Faelten, David Diamond, and the editors of *Prevention* magazine, *Take Control of Your Life: A Complete Guide to Stress Relief* (Emmaus, Penn.: Rodale Press, 1988), p. 309.

21. David D. Burns, M.D., *Feeling Good: The New Mood Therapy* (New York: New American Library, 1980).

22. Daniel Goleman and Joel Gurin, eds., *Mind/Body Medicine: How to Use Your Mind for Better Health* (New York: Consumer Reports Books, 1993), p. 364.

23. Ezra Taft Benson, *Teachings of Ezra Taft Benson* (Salt Lake City: Bookcraft, 1988), p. 401.

24. Neal A. Maxwell, *Deposition of a Disciple* (Salt Lake City: Deseret Book, 1976), p. 98.

25. Marvin J. Ashton, *Conference Report,* April 1986, p. 86.

One of the important things that differentiates man from animal is that he laughs.

— Malcolm Muggeridge

CHAPTER

14

The Healing Power of Humor and Laughter

Known Church-wide for his sometimes irreverent sense of humor, Elder J. Golden Kimball once took the podium in general conference, surveyed the crowd assembled in the Salt Lake Tabernacle, and quipped, "The Lord Himself must like a joke, or he wouldn't have made some of you people."

Elder Neal A. Maxwell, who said the living prophets he had known all had a sense of humor,[1] challenged us to "be persons of good works and good will, cultivating a sense of humor that allows for critics."[2]

On another occasion, he wrote:

> How wonderful it is to see those whose sense of humor includes the capacity to see themselves and their frailties laughingly—not in the chronic, self-deprecating, biting way. Those who can see themselves and their incongruities with smiles (not sarcasm) suggest to the rest of us that they have an inner security, and this encourages the rest of us to take heart in a world in which too many of us are much too serious about ourselves and in which too much of the laughter is nervous laughter.[3]

President Abraham Lincoln, who called good humor the "oxygen of the soul," once said, "With the fearful strain that is on me night and day, if I did not laugh I should die."

Everyone loves a good joke, and everyone loves to laugh. Mark Twain once penned the sentiment that "against the assault of laughter nothing can stand." What the great American humorist and author believed more than a hundred years ago is being proved today by some of our most gifted scientists: a sense of humor, and the laughter that accompanies it, can actually banish pain and keep us well.

Laughter may *seem* simple, but it's actually a complex physical process. *Health and Fitness* News Service writer Robert Brody asks us to remember the last time we had "an out-and-out belly laugh, a real fall-on-the-floor special." He writes:

> You were some sight. Your mouth was twisted open, your tongue was stuck out halfway, your lips were pulled back and your nostrils were flared. Though you felt pleasure, your face suggested pain. Your cheeks turned red and you doubled over, gasping. Your stomach, chest, and ribs ached. You were helpless, unable even to speak. You looked as if you'd just been punched in the gut.

Let's take a look at exactly what happens when we laugh. Once we are ready to laugh, the muscles in the face that control expressions start to contort, says Brody. Muscles throughout the body contract like fists. The muscles of the vocal cord, designed for intelligible sound, cannot coordinate. The throat opens, ready to vibrate. The diaphragm tenses up in anticipation of respiratory spasms. According to Brody, "air in your body billows until you feel pressure building up in your lungs. Trying to hold in a laugh is no less than a violation against nature—rarely successful."

Once the laugh gets into full gear, writes Brody, "your breathing is interrupted for a station break. Your lower jaw vibrates. A blast of air gusts into your throat, flinging mucus against the walls of your windpipe. Pandemonium! Out comes your laugh, in some cases clocked at 170 miles per hour. You issue a strange machine-gun sound, almost a violent bark."

Once in the throes of a full-bodied laugh, our bodies buck. Our torsos flex. Our arms flail, our hands slap our thighs. Our eyes squeeze out tears. "You puff and rasp with symphonic regularity," Brody writes. "You can hardly stand so much glee coursing through you. You're wobbly in the knees, wheezing like an asthmatic. Pleading for mercy, you collapse on the nearest sofa. Sounds like fun, no?"

Laughter is one of the best exercises around. It's simple. It requires no training or special equipment. We don't have to do it at the gym or on the track or on a Nautilus machine. All we need, in fact, is a sense of humor. Stanford Medical School psychiatrist William Fry, Jr., says that laughter causes huffing and puffing, speeds up the heart rate, raises blood pressure, accelerates breathing, increases oxygen consumption, gives the muscles of the stomach and face a workout, and relaxes the muscles that aren't used in laughing. Laughter is especially valuable for strengthening the heart muscle—and, Fry says, *just twenty seconds of laughter* is the cardiovascular equivalent of *three minutes of strenuous rowing.*[4]

Laughter provides what some experts have called "a total inner body workout," and the health benefits are obvious. One of the best known examples of the power of laughter is the late *Saturday Review* editor Norman Cousins. When symptoms of achiness, fatigue, and fever worsened instead of getting better, he sought medical help. The diagnosis was devastating: a potentially life-threatening disease that affected all the connective tissues of the body. The disease was so advanced that he was already having trouble just moving his joints. His physician told him he probably wouldn't recover.

Instead of accepting the prognosis that sentenced him to pain and then death, Cousins decided to take things into his own hands. He designed a program of positive thinking, nutritious foods, and laughter as a painkiller.

In fact, he discovered laughter was the most effective painkiller he could find. Ten minutes of hearty laughter (usually prompted by old "Candid Camera" reruns) provided two hours of pain-free sleep. Even more remarkably, he found that the swelling in his tissues was reduced after each laughter session.

A decade later—fully recovered and vigorous—he wrote of his experience. He gave laughter part of the credit for his miraculous recovery. Following his claims, a number of scientists set out to test his theory that laughter could relieve pain. Research shows that there are several likely reasons why laughter relieves pain. For one, laughter relaxes muscles, and pain often involves muscle tension. And laughter stimulates the brain to release endorphins, potent natural painkillers estimated to be two hundred times more powerful than morphine. Endorphins also reduce swelling and can stimulate the immune system. They're the chemicals responsible for the famed "runner's high," and researchers now believe there may be a very real and similar "laugher's high."

Further research on laughter has revealed what may be one of its most important benefits: it apparently enhances the immune system. Laughter appears to boost the production of chemicals that enhance immunity, and it suppresses the hormones that weaken immunity (the stress hormones). Psychologist Robert Ornstein and physician David Sobel point out, "When confronted with a threatening situation, animals have essentially two choices: to flee or fight. Humans have a third alternative: to laugh."[5]

Studies have measured the effects of laughter on the immune system, and scientists have found that laughter:[6]

- Activates the T lymphocytes, the cells that attack foreign invaders.
- Increases production of both the cells that turn on the immune response and those that turn it off when it's no longer needed.
- Increases *both the number and activity* of natural killer cells, the immune cells that conduct surveillance against tumor cells and viruses in the body.
- Increases the amount of IgA (immunoglobulin A), which helps protect against upper respiratory tract infections.

- Increases the amount of gamma interferon, a substance that turns on various parts of the immune system.
- Increases a number of other immune components, some for as long as a day following the laughter.

Laughter has also been shown to relieve stress, in part because the body doesn't produce stress hormones as efficiently during laughter. The stress-relieving effect of laughter doesn't last just while you're chuckling, either. Experts agree that the ability to laugh to dispel stress lasts long after the laugh and can actually help build an immunity to stress.

American actress Ethel Barrymore maintained that "You grow up the day you have the first real laugh—at yourself." Some of the biggest crises we experience as adults turn into some of our funniest moments; the mere passage of time transforms them. Top stand-up comic Judy Carter maintains that "there's a little bit of stand-up comic in everyone; the performance comes not when you're having a fight, but in telling a friend afterward."[7]

Antioch University professor Harvey Mindess, an expert in humor, points out that "humor at its best encourages a broad perspective on life. It provides a view of the ironies that abound, of the fact that nobody and nothing is as it seems. And recognizing life's zaniness encourages flexibility and adaptability, rather than rigidity and brittleness."[8]

In addition to its health benefits, humor and laughter provide tremendous psychological benefits as well. Humor enhances self-esteem; people with a good sense of humor are able to look at their own failings in a humorous way, and they are able to laugh at themselves. It promotes creativity; people with a good sense of humor are generally more creative, especially in the way they solve life's problems. Edward deBono, one of the world's leading authorities on creativity, says that humor and the creative process are actually the same: they recognize the value of the absurd or the creative idea only in hindsight.

One University of Maryland psychologist proved the value of humor to creativity. She had one group of volunteers watch a math film, and a second watch a clip of hilarious television "bloopers." Then she gave each group a box of tacks, a candle, and a book of matches with the charge to use their "equipment" to attach the candle to the wall so it could be lit without dripping any wax. The volunteers who had watched the funny clip attacked the problem with much greater efficiency and creativity. One volunteer emptied the box of tacks, tacked the box to the corkboard wall, and used it as a candleholder.[9]

Humor also improves negotiation and decision-making skills; negotiators who have a sense of humor are less anxious, have fewer contentions, and are more able to reach solutions that please both parties. It helps us maintain a sense of balance; renowned American clergyman Henry Ward Beecher wrote that a person without a sense of humor "is like a wagon without springs—jolted by every pebble in the sand." And it improves both individual and group performance, especially when the humor is directly related to the task at hand.[10]

A sense of humor also bestows a sense of power, relieves stress, and improves coping ability. Psychologist Samuel Janus and scientists Seymour and Rhoda Fisher cite numerous examples of famous "funny people" who used humor to cope with deep psychological pain.[11] For example, Totie Field's mother died when she was five, David Steinberg's brother was killed in Vietnam, Jackie Gleason's father deserted him, W. C. Fields ran away from home because his father was going to kill him, Dudley Moore was born with a club foot, Art Buchwald's mother died when he was very young, and Carol Burnett's parents were both alcoholics who fought constantly.

Charlie Chaplin, too, found solace in humor:

> Raised in one of the poorest sections of London, he was five years old when his father died of alcoholism; after that his mother went mad. Chaplin used these gloomy memories in his films and turned them into comedic gems. Who could forget the scene in "Gold Rush," for example, where he eats a boiled leather shoe for dinner because no other food is available?[12]

Though we don't often consider Church leaders as great examples of humor, Church historian Leonard J. Arrington pointed out that the Prophet Joseph Smith had an endearing sense of humor. Addressing an audience at Brigham Young University, he said:

> The Prophet recognized as unhealthy the mind which lacked balance, perspective, and humor. In the society of his day there were many earnest people who habitually looked on the serious side of things that had no serious side, who regarded humor as incompatible with religion. . . . But Joseph Smith saw humor and religion as quite reconcilable. As he saw it, once one acknowledges that there is something beyond laughter—a core of life that is solemn, serious, and tender—there is still plenty of room for jesting. . . .
>
> Joseph's well-adjusted nature was infectious. Those brought up in the strict, long-faced, pious tradition soon found themselves liberated so they could fulfill their foreordained roles of being leaders of the Saints. Converts who had been brought up with less enjoyment of life and spontaneity were unfrozen; their experiences and enjoyments were expanded. . . . Religion was not to confine spirits, he pointed out, but to expand them. . . .
>
> Certainly the calling of prophet was one of such high seriousness that its responsibilities could well have weighted down a less vital mind. But it was humor which helped Joseph to dispose of conflicts and problems that did not really matter. The Prophet was deeply serious, but he was not solemn; he believed an unduly solemn person had lost something of the image of his Creator.[13]

To have more fun in life, we might try following these suggestions from Leigh Anne Jasheway, coordinator of health promotion at the University of Texas Health Science Center at Houston:

- Making a pledge to laugh out loud or to make someone else laugh at least ten times a day.
- Once a week, setting aside time to call someone who always adds fun to the day.
- Reading our favorite comics in the newspaper every day.

- Making regular dates with a friend or spouse to do any recreation we both enjoy.
- Doing something silly at least once a week.
- Starting a humor collection: jokes, clippings, cartoons, cards, books, or videos.
- Renting funny movies.
- Trying to find the humor in every predicament.
- Keeping a "fun first-aid kit" full of things like modeling clay, bubbles, puzzles, brain teasers, and other things we love to do.
- Finally, recalling all the fun we had as children!

Perhaps one of the best suggestions is to create what Loretta LaRoche calls a "humor survival kit," and one of her best tools, she says, always gets a laugh:

> Buy something silly you can put on (a pair of Groucho Marx glasses are my favorite). Put them on in situations where you tend to awfulize. I wear mine driving through Boston, especially when I have to merge. People always let me in. Food shopping is another favorite. Among others, going to the dentist, the doctor, staff meetings, talking to your mate, the children, a coworker. When things have really reached the limits of your endurance, go into a bathroom, look into the mirror, put on your glasses, and ask yourself this question: "How serious is this?"[14]

As Elder Neal A. Maxwell wrote, a disciple of Christ "is serious about the living of his life, but he is happy and of good cheer. His humor is the humor of hope and his mirth is the uplifting mirth of morality, not the cutting cleverness of despair."[15]

Of utmost importance, concluded President Hugh B. Brown, is the genuine nature of our humor:

> Life is really a battle between fear and faith, pessimism and optimism. Fear and pessimism paralyze men with skepticism and futility. One must have a sense of humor to be an optimist in times like these. . . . But your good humor must

be real, not simulated. Let your smiles come from the heart and they will become contagious. You may see men on the street any day whose laugh is only a frozen grin with nothing in it but teeth. Men without humor tend to forget their source, lose sight of their goal, and with no lubrication in their mental crankshafts, they must drop out of the race.[16]

END NOTES

1. Neal A. Maxwell, *Deposition of a Disciple* (Salt Lake City: Deseret Book, 1976), p. 52.
2. Neal A. Maxwell, *We Will Prove Them Herewith* (Salt Lake City: Deseret Book, 1982), p. 97.
3. Neal A. Maxwell, *For the Power Is in Them: Mormon Musings* (Salt Lake City: Deseret Book, 1970), p. 25.
4. C.W. Metcalf and Roma Felible, *Lighten Up: Survival Skills for People Under Pressure* (Reading, Mass.: Addison-Wesley Publishing, Inc.), p. 9.
5. Robert Ornstein and David Sobel, *Healthy Pleasures* (Reading, Mass.: Addison-Wesley Publishing, Inc., 1989), p. 218.
6. "New Discoveries in Psychoneuroimmunology: An Interview with Dr. Lee S. Berk," *Humor and Health Letter,* Vol. 3, No. 6, November/December 1994, pp. 2-4.
7. Caryl S. Avery, "Lighten Up," *Self,* September 1988, pp. 150-57.
8. Ibid., p. 157.
9. Susan Lang, "Laughing Matters—At Work," *American Health,* September 1988, p. 46.
10. Ibid.
11. Allen Klein, *The Healing Power of Humor* (Los Angeles: Jeremy P. Tarcher, Inc., 1989).
12. Ibid., pp. 5-6.
13. Leonard J. Arrington, "The Looseness of Zion: Joseph Smith and the Lighter View," in *Speeches of the Year, 1974* (Provo, Utah: BYU Press, 1975), pp. 294-95, 299.
14. Loretta LaRoche, "Fully Human, Fully Alive with Humor, Compassion, and Love," *The Psychology of Health, Immunity, and Disease,* Vol. A, p. 326,

in Proceedings of the Sixth International Conference of the National Institute for the Clinical Application of Behavioral Medicine, Hilton Head, S.C., 1994.

15. Neal A. Maxwell, *Notwithstanding My Weakness* (Salt Lake City: Deseret Book, 1981), p. 122.

16. Hugh B. Brown, *The Abundant Life* (Salt Lake City: Bookcraft, 1965), p. 50.

Humor at its best encourages a broad perspective on life . . . Recognizing life's zaniness encourages flexibility and adaptability, rather than rigidity and brittleness.

— DR. HARVEY MINDESS

The Lord wants us to be filled with hope—not just because it points us to a brighter tomorrow, but because it changes the quality of our lives today. . . . This is the nature of hope. We do all we can, and then the Lord stretches forth his hand and touches our lives with light and courage and, most of all, hope.

— DWAN J. YOUNG

CHAPTER

15

The Healing Power of Hope

Former *Saturday Review* editor Norman Cousins, who successfully fought his own terminal illness, spent the last decades of his life working with and studying people diagnosed with serious disease. Of the reality of hope, he said:

> People tell me not to offer hope unless I know hope to be real. I don't know enough to say that hope can't be real. I'm not sure anyone knows enough to deny hope. I have seen too many cases these past ten years when death predictions were delivered from high professional station only to be gloriously refuted by patients for reasons having less to do with tangible biology than with the human spirit, admittedly a vague term but one that may well be the greatest force of all within the human arsenal.[1]

Hope—defined as "a wealth of optimism, a want of fear"—is apparently one of the strongest influences on health and the human body and the defining purpose of the human spirit. David Steindl Rast defined it aptly when he said, "Hope looks at all things the way a mother looks at her child—with a passion for the possible."

True hope, wrote Elder Neal A. Maxwell, focuses us on the great realities, on "things as they really are," and frees us from anxiety and despair. Hope "stiffens, not slackens, the spine. It is anticipation that turns into day-by-day determination. It is an eager and an enthusiastic expectation based upon a dependable and justifiable object of hope, the . . . Lord Jesus Christ."[2]

University of Kansas psychologist C. Rick Snyder claims that hope is more than—and indeed, is quite different from—a vague feeling of optimism. Instead, hope is a pragmatic, goal-oriented attitude, a stance people assume in the face of difficulty. It generates the means to overcome the difficulty, to reach the goal.[3]

Psychologist Robert Ornstein and physician David Sobel define hope as "a special type of positive expectation. Unlike denial, which involves a negation of reality, hope is an active way of coping with threatening situations by focusing on the positive. No matter how dark or grim a situation may appear, certain people seem to be able to extract the positive aspects and concentrate on them. They fill their mind with hopeful scenarios, stories with happy endings, or lucky outcomes."[4]

Elder Neal A. Maxwell compared our gospel perspective of hope to the marvel of satellite telecommunications, which can help us predict the weather and can even provide photographs of approaching storm fronts. Yet, he wrote, "just because we know a winter storm is coming, it is no less cold; the snow still falls with all of the attending and harsh consequences." The overview provided by the satellite, however, lets us know "that the storm front, however severe, will pass away."

That perspective is much like the one provided by the gospel, which brings with it a sure sense of hope:

> Likewise, the storm fronts that come into our lives will not last forever. We can surmount the drifts of difficulties and we can hold out if we maintain our perspective and our faith. But while we are in the midst of all these things,

> the experiences that can be for our long-term good are very, very real. We may feel that such are simply more than we can bear. Yet if we have faith in an all-knowing and all-loving God, we understand he will not give us more than we can bear.
>
> Just as we know there is a sun just beyond today's cloud cover, so we must not doubt the continued, watchful, and tutoring presence of The Son in spite of the stormy seasons in our lives.[5]

Hope sets in motion an entirely new set of expectations: it boosts belief about what can be achieved, and it makes possible the setting of new goals. Hope is the belief that something is obtainable. As one writer stated, social movements aren't caused by failure and frustration, but from rising strength and what *Psychology Today* editor-in-chief George Harris calls "the snake of hope." Simply put, "prison riots start when the food is getting better, not worse."[6]

A report published in *Medical World News* claimed that "hope can play an important role in vulnerability to disease, the course of illness, and possibly in determining whether a patient lives or dies."[7] In the same report, University of Arkansas psychiatrist Fred O. Henker said that "whether we acknowledge the influence of hope or not, it's real, and may even determine the life or death outcome of a patient."

Hope has a powerful influence on physical health and well-being. Medical lore is filled with examples of "terminal" patients who, filled with hope, defied all medical odds. Some lived months or years longer than predicted. Some defied the odds completely: they lived and they were healed.

One possible explanation is that hope is not just a mental state; it causes specific chemical changes in the body that make the immune system stronger and can even influence the way internal organs work.

Norman Cousins is perhaps best known for his research into what he called "the biology of hope." He explained that *hope* is actually tremendous *expectation,* and that it has powerful influence over the human body. One of his favorite examples involved a golfer who suffered a heart attack at the Rancho Golf Course near Cousins' home.[8] As the ambulance arrived, Cousins walked over to see what was happening.

The man was ashen and trembling. As Cousins recalled it, the paramedics worked systematically and methodically. They administered oxygen. They hooked the man up to a cardiograph, which revealed a dangerously rapid heartbeat. But "no one was talking to the poor fellow." So Cousins leaned over and lied to the man.

> I put my hand on his shoulder and I said, "Sir, you've got a great heart." He opened his eyes and he looked at me and asked, "Why do you say that?" I said, "Well, I can see on the cardiograph that you've got a wonderful heart. What happened is that it's been very hot out here today. You've probably dehydrated on the golf course and that upset the balance of sodium and potassium that provides the electricity that your heart needs for the next flip. But you're in good hands now. In a few minutes, you'll be in one of the best hospitals in the world. You'll be just fine."

Within *thirty seconds* the cardiogram began to change. In just two minutes, the man's heartbeat had slowed almost to normal.

Hope has been shown in countless studies to be a potent factor in healing. Dr. Isaac Djerassi, the scientist who discovered the treatment for both childhood leukemia and bone cancer, maintains that hope is essential to healing, and that both the patient and the physician must be hopeful:

> I can say from my own experience that patients who have given up, who have come to me feeling defeated and desperate, feeling that nothing can possibly help them, have often made their own prediction come true. The fighter-type patients who are willing to try anything that has a chance to help them, who have real faith in their survival, always do better. The same thing holds true of doctors. Some of the doctors get discouraged too early and give up on patients who could still be helped. When you

> pick a doctor, make certain he's a fighter, someone who will stand by you and fight for you.[9]

"Why do some excellent, scientifically oriented doctors fail in practice whereas others, whom both you and I know give inferior care, achieve enormous success?" wrote Dr. M. G. Jacoby of Brookhaven Memorial Hospital in "A Father's Letter to a New Intern," published in the *Journal of the American Medical Association.* "You know the answer as well as I do. They give their patients what they really need, hope, a shot of psychopenicillin that should be injected at every visit."[10]

A chilling story about the power of hope was told by Army medical officer Major F. Harold Kushner, who was captured by the Viet Cong when his helicopter was shot down over North Vietnam in November 1967.[11] Seriously injured, he was sent to "First Camp," where twenty-seven Americans were eventually imprisoned. As he described it:

> At any given time there were about eleven men who lived in a bamboo hut, sleeping on one crowded bamboo bed about sixteen feet across. The basic diet was three small cups of red, rotten, vermin-infested rice a day. Within the first year the average prisoner lost 40 to 50 percent of his body weight, and acquired running sores and atrophied muscles. There were two prominent killers: malnutrition and helplessness.

By the time Kushner arrived at camp, a twenty-four-year-old paratrooper named Robert had already been there for two years. A "rugged and intelligent" corporal, he was down to ninety pounds and was forced to make long, shoeless treks every day with ninety pounds of manioc root on his back. But despite appalling malnutrition and a terrible skin disease, he remained in very good physical and mental health. The cause of his good condition was clear to Kushner: Robert knew that the Viet Cong periodically released a few cooperative prisoners as an example to the rest. The camp commander had indicated that Robert was next, that he'd be released within six months. Simply stated, his hope kept him going.

Sure enough, six months later a high-ranking Viet Cong official came to give the group a political course, and it was understood that the top student would be released. Robert was chosen to head the thought-reform group. He made the required statements and was told to expect release within a month.

But the month came and went, and Robert gradually sensed a change in the way the guards treated him. Finally he realized he'd been deceived, that he had been used and was not going to be released. Before Kushner's eyes, Robert changed from a man who was filled with hope and whose physical condition was strong despite overwhelming odds to a prisoner who gave up hope:

> [Robert] stopped working and showed signs of severe depression; he refused food and lay on his bed in a fetal position, sucking his thumb. His fellow prisoners tried to bring him around. They hugged him, babied him, and when this didn't work, tried to bring him out of his stupor with their fists. He defecated and urinated in the bed. After a few weeks, it was apparent to Kushner that Robert was [about to die]. . . . In the early hours of a November morning he lay dying in Kushner's arms. For the first time in days his eyes focused and he spoke: "Doc, Post Office Box 161, Texarkana, Texas. Mom, Dad, I love you very much. Barbara, I forgive you." Within seconds, he was dead.

Though he was a physician, Kushner didn't have the tools to perform an autopsy. In his professional opinion, the specific cause of Robert's death was psychological, not physical. "Hope of release sustained Robert," he summed up. "When he gave up hope, when he believed all his efforts had failed and would continue to fail, he died."[12]

In his book *Human Options,* Cousins observes that we "must never underestimate the capacity of the human mind and body to regenerate—even when the prospects seem most wretched." And, he says, essential medical treatment "will be far more effective if people put their creative hopes, their faith, and their confidence fully to work in behalf of their recovery."[13] As Thomas Campbell wrote, "Cease, every joy, to glimmer on my mind. But leave, oh leave, the light of hope behind."

A special kind of hope is a *fighting spirit*: the refusal to lapse into hopelessness or surrender to despair. A person with fighting spirit refuses to give up, despite the odds. While fighters aren't better or more capable than anyone else, they don't give up as easily as others do. In study after study, such fighters have been shown to enjoy better health and live longer, even when physicians and laboratory tests say they shouldn't.

Researchers aren't exactly sure why a fighting spirit works so well. There are probably many reasons. For one, people are not born fighters; they become fighters. Dr. Wayne Eisom, head of cardiothoracic surgery at New York Hospital-Cornell Medical Center, gives an example: all surgical patients are asked to take a deep breath and cough the day after surgery. It hurts tremendously, but it's crucial—it opens collapsed air sacs in the lungs. "A patient who is a fighter will cough hard and often," Eisom says. "The other kind of patient won't, and very often dies of pneumonia."

Dr. Willibald Nagler, chief psychiatrist at New York Hospital-Cornell Medical Center, says that if a patient in a wheelchair is determined to walk again "no matter what, he probably will. He'll get up out of his wheelchair and try to walk. Maybe he'll fall down, but he'll pick himself up and try again. The patient who keeps moaning, 'I'm never going to walk again' won't even try."

Another important factor may be at work: when a physician sees that a patient is a fighter, he or she is much more likely to join in the fight. "Doctors will go the extra mile for a patient who is a fighter," says Dr. Phillip Casson of New York University Medical Center, one of the nation's most distinguished surgeons. "They'll operate when the odds against success are overwhelming. They'll come to the hospital at two A.M. to see how a patient is getting along. You've got a much better chance for a long, healthy, and happy life if you're willing to fight for it."

Perhaps one of the greatest examples of a fighting spirit is former New York City Opera director Beverly Sills, who has faced incredible personal tragedy in her life. Both her children were born deaf; one was also mentally handicapped. She survived cancer. An arsonist destroyed her new home. All the while, she says, she "became a much more rational person despite all the irrationality of the events. I had lived through the worst day of my life. I felt that, from that time on, everything else had to be up."[14]

As Eleanor Roosevelt said, "You gain strength, courage, and confidence by every experience in which you really stop to look fear in the face. You are able to say to yourself, 'I lived through this horror. I can take the next thing that comes along.' You must do the thing you think you cannot do."

In summing up her life's philosophy, Beverly Sills remarks that "everything does not happen for the best. But I do think there's a reason for everything. We poor mortals just aren't clever enough to know what that reason is. I must say that I still love life. There are an awful lot of good things ahead of us, and there are some wonderful things behind us. Every crisis is a challenge. You just have to shake your fist and meet it."[15]

Her philosophy is echoed by President Ezra Taft Benson, who challenged, "We must not lose hope. Hope is an anchor to the souls of men. Satan would have us cast away that anchor. In this way he can bring discouragement and surrender."[16]

As Latter-day Saints, the essence of our hope—both for and beyond this life—rests with the Savior of the world. As President Ezra Taft Benson taught, "only Jesus Christ is uniquely qualified to provide hope."[17] And, as the Apostle Paul so clearly wrote, the "Lord Jesus Christ . . . is our hope" (1 Timothy 1:1).

Part of that hope lies with what happened in Gethsemane. As President Spencer W. Kimball taught, "the principle of repentance—of rising again whenever we fall, brushing ourselves off, and setting off again on that upward trail—is the basis for our hope. It is through repentance that the Lord Jesus Christ can work his healing miracle, infusing us with strength when we are weak, health when we are sick, hope when we are downhearted, love when we feel empty, and understanding when we search for truth."[18]

Today, said President Kimball, "is just a grain of sand in the Sahara of eternity. We have also a hope in Christ for the eternity that lies ahead." The other part of our hope, then, focuses on what happened at Golgotha. Much of hopelessness can be traced to a failure to properly understand the plan of salvation, including the fact of an existence both before and after this one. "When individuals are without hope regarding the life to come, death becomes terribly controlling so far as this life is concerned," wrote Elder Neal A. Maxwell. "The second estate is lived out as if it were a final and concluding exclamation point rather than another comma in the continuum of man's existence."[19]

Brigham Young told the early Saints:

> When faithful Latter-day Saints come to the end of their earthly existence, "we know that if our earthly house of this tabernacle were dissolved, we have a building of God, an house not made with hands, eternal in the heavens." The faithful Latter-day Saint knows that the dissolution of this mortal house will introduce his immortal spirit to freedom from death and punishment, and to the enjoyment of the society of the spirits of just men made perfect. To a person who has such a glorious hope, everything is bright and beautiful.[20]

"Men are born, they live for an hour of glory, and die," said President Gordon B. Hinckley. "Most throughout their lives are teased by various hopes; and among all the hopes of men in all ages of time, none is so great as the hope of immortality. The empty tomb that first Easter morning brought the most comforting assurance that can come into man's heart."[21]

Our hope for life eternal, and that hope alone, wrote Elder Neal A. Maxwell, is what "permits us to 'endure well' to the end—knowing that the end is but a glorious beginning!"[22] As Nephi so eloquently taught, "Wherefore, ye must press forward with a steadfastness in Christ, having a perfect brightness of hope. . . . Wherefore, if ye shall press forward, feasting upon the word of Christ, and endure to the end, behold, thus saith the Father: Ye shall have eternal life" (2 Nephi 31:16, 20).

Of the Lord Jesus Christ, Elder Bruce R. McConkie wrote:

> In and through and by and because of him we and all men have a hope of peace in this life and eternal glory in the world to come. He is our Hope. Without him we would have no hope of immortality, no hope of eternal life, no hope of the continuation of the family unit, no hope of eternal progress, no hope of exaltation, no hope of any good thing. All the hopes of the righteous of all the ages center in him.[23]

END NOTES

1. Norman Cousins, *Head First: The Biology of Hope* (New York: E. P. Dutton, 1989), pp. 65-66.
2. Neal A. Maxwell, *Notwithstanding My Weakness* (Salt Lake City: Deseret Book, 1981), p. 49.
3. "Where There's Hope, There's Life," *Berkeley Wellness Letter*, March 1992, pp. 2-3.
4. Robert Ornstein and David Sobel, *The Healing Brain* (New York: Simon and Schuster, 1987), p. 243.
5. Neal A. Maxwell, *Even As I Am* (Salt Lake City: Deseret Book, 1985), p. 102.
6. Gilbert Brim, "Losing and Winning," *Psychology Today,* September 1988, pp. 48-52.
7. "Studies Show Hope Can Play Role in a Patient's Risk, Illness, Death," *Medical World News,* June 11, 1984, pp. 101-102.
8. "Hope: That Sustainer of Man," *Executive Health,* Section II, Vol. 20,

No. 3, 1983, pp. 1-4.
9. "Hope: That Sustainer of Man," *Executive Health,* Section II, Vol. 20, No. 3, 1983, pp. 1-4.
10. Ibid.
11. Story related in Martin E. P. Seligman, *Helplessness: On Depression, Development and Death* (W. H. Freeman and Company, 1975), p. 34.
12. Ibid., pp. 35-37.
13. Norman Cousins, *Human Options* (New York: W. W. Norton, 1981), p. 69.
14. Beverly Sills and Katrine Ames, "Facing Down Disaster," *Longevity,* September 1990, p. 69.
15. Ibid.
16. Ezra Taft Benson, *Teachings of Ezra Taft Benson* (Salt Lake City: Bookcraft, 1988), p. 398.
17. Ibid., p. 66.
18. Spencer W. Kimball, *The Teachings of Spencer W. Kimball,* comp. by Edward L. Kimball (Salt Lake City: Bookcraft, 1982), p. 106.
19. Neal A. Maxwell, *Deposition of a Disciple* (Salt Lake City: Deseret Book, 1976), p. 14.
20. Brigham Young, *Journal of Discourses,* Vol. 11 (Liverpool, England: F. D. Richards et al., 1864), pp. 15-16.
21. Gordon B. Hinckley, *Conference Report,* April 1969, p. 59.
22. Neal A. Maxwell, *Notwithstanding My Weakness* (Salt Lake City: Deseret Book, 1981), p. 49.
23. Bruce R. McConkie, *The Promised Messiah: The First Coming of Christ* (Salt Lake City: Deseret Book, 1978), p. 183.

To Be Spiritually Minded Is Life Eternal

Developing spirituality and attuning ourselves to the highest influences of godliness is not an easy matter. It takes time and frequently involves a struggle. It will not happen by chance, but is accomplished only through deliberate effort and by calling upon God and keeping his commandments. . . . Spirituality is not acquired suddenly. It is the consequence of a succession of right choices. It is the harvest of a righteous life.

— DALLIN H. OAKS

CHAPTER

16

The Healing Power of Spirituality

An old Spanish proverb aptly warns, "He that loseth wealth, loseth much. He that loseth friends, loseth more. But he that loseth spirituality, loseth all."

One dictionary defines *spirituality* as "the faculty that gives a feeling of confidence; sense of the spiritual; belief in divine things; an inclination to interpret prospects of promise in one's own favor."

According to President David O. McKay, spirituality, "the highest acquisition of the soul," is "the divine in man—the supreme, crowning gift that makes him king of all created things." It entails "victory over self" and "communion with the Infinite."[1]

President Ezra Taft Benson defined spirituality as "being in tune with the Spirit of the Lord."[2] Elder Bruce R. McConkie wrote, "Spirituality is that state of holiness, purity, and relative perfection which enables men to enjoy the near-constant companionship of the Lord's Spirit; truly spiritual men walk in the light of personal revelation and enjoy the frequent promptings of the Holy Ghost."[3] And Hugh Nibley wrote that "the highest state of spirituality is to be filled with the spirit of God, the Holy Ghost. . . ."[4]

President David O. McKay gave a clue to the attributes that accompany spirituality when he said:

> Every noble impulse, every unselfish expression of love; every brave suffering for the right; every surrender of self to something higher than self; every loyalty to an ideal; every unselfish devotion to principle; every helpfulness to humanity; every act of self-control; every fine courage of the soul, undefeated by pretense or policy, but by being, doing, and living of good for the very good's sake—that is spirituality.[5]

Spirituality, said another, "is that liveliness of spirit that intensifies appreciation of the beautiful, deepens loyalty to truth and kindles love for the good; it puts the heart in harmony with the moral forces of the world; promotes delight in the realization of high ideals; and quickens in the heart the joyous glory of being in actual partnership with God in the purification and ennoblement of mankind."[6]

Science, too, is recognizing the phenomenon we know as spirituality. As Albert Einstein so eloquently put it, "Everyone who is seriously involved in the pursuit of science becomes convinced that a Spirit is manifest in the Laws of the Universe—a Spirit vastly superior to that of man, and one in the face of which we, with our modest powers, must feel humble."

The attribute of spirituality changes the way we behave: we draw progressively away from worldliness and steadily toward our Father in Heaven. Alma describes this as a "mighty change" wrought in the heart as a result of spirituality (see Alma 5:11-14). As our spirituality increases, we are influenced less by the opinions of men, more by the desire to savor the companionship of the Spirit. The attitude of spirituality changes the way we think; we concentrate less on the things of mortality, more on the things of eternity. In his second letter to the Corinthians, Paul wrote, "We look not at the things which are seen, but at the things which are not seen: for the things which are seen are temporal; but the things which are not seen are eternal" (2 Corinthians 4:18).

As Elder Dallin H. Oaks wrote, spirituality even changes the way we look at things: "Spirituality is a lens through which we view life and a gauge by which we evaluate it," he taught. "Our lens gives its special tint to all we see."[7]

Spirituality changes our ability to give as well as to receive[8]: we begin to understand that along with receiving love and joy and peace and fulfillment, through our experiences we can give those things as well. We can give peace to another by offering words of encouragement or forgiveness. We can give joy by giving someone else a deeply deserved gift. We can share love by countless acts of sacrifice, by putting others before ourselves, by considering someone else first. Spirituality can be manifest by listening to a friend's heartaches, walking with a child, or leaving a box of groceries on the porch of a young family whose husband lost his job. Spirituality can be enhanced by sitting at the edge of a meadow studded with wildflowers, befriending someone who is lonely, or listening to a symphony.

Finally, spirituality changes the way we feel about ourselves—the way we regard our place in the universe, among our fellow citizens. Yale surgeon and cancer specialist Bernie Siegel pointed out the tremendous freedom spirituality brings:

> You always have a choice about how you feel. Listen to Jesse Jackson say that you may not have chosen to be down, but you have a choice as to whether you want to try to get up. . . . Listen to Mahatma Gandhi, who said, "Let us not kill our enemies but kill their desire to kill." And so you have a choice about how you behave, whether you are in prison, whether you are in a concentration camp, or whether you are sick. You have a choice.[9]

Spirituality entails developing our spiritual nature to its fullest potential. Spirituality, with its attendant spiritual health, is not the same as physical health. You can enjoy optimum spiritual health even as you battle the ravages of terminal cancer.

Regardless of physical condition, the quest for spirituality is never in vain, wrote *Psychology Today* editor Mark Barasch.

> To find it, we may have to forsake, once and for all, that misapprehension that sees Good in what aggrandizes us, Beauty in what is unblemished, Wholeness only in what is intact. For those who can summon the courage to tread a path with heart, illness's dark passage may provide a glimpse not only of what it is like to become whole, but what it means to be fully human.[10]

In fact, spirituality may have an immense impact on physical health. In addition to the power of the mind to influence health, "there is another aspect of healing that needs to be addressed: the spiritual aspect," wrote renowned radiation oncologist O. Carl Simonton, following years of research. "The dictionary defines *spirit* as the life principle, especially in humans, and the feelings and motivating part of our lives. . . . Our work with patients has demonstrated that health involves body, mind, *and* spirit. And while the mind alone can be used to influence the physical state, it is used most effectively when it is aware of spirit."[11]

What, then, is this essence that can provide obvious health benefits? Physician Rachel Naomi Remen, medical director of the Commonweal Cancer Help Program and a member of the Scientific Advisory Board for the Institute of Noetic Sciences, says it may be easiest to define the spiritual by defining what it isn't. The spiritual, she says, is not the moral. Nor is it the ethical. The spiritual is also not the psychic, nor is it the religious.

The spiritual, she says, is inclusive. It is the deepest sense of belonging and participation. "We all participate in the spiritual at all times, whether we know it or not. There's no place to go to be separated from the spiritual. . . . The most important thing in defining spirit is the recognition that spirit is an essential need of human nature. There is something in all of us that seeks the spiritual. This yearning varies in strength from person to person but it is always there in everyone. And so healing becomes possible."[12]

The essence she describes is the light of Christ, "the light which is in all things, which giveth life to all things, which is the law by which all things are governed, even the power of God" (D&C 88:13). As President Joseph Fielding Smith described it, it is "the light by which the worlds are controlled, by which they are made." Every man and woman, he taught, receives the light of Christ and is guided by it.[13] It bears testimony to each of us that the Lord is "not far from every one of us" (Acts 17:27).

Healing is made possible by the light of Christ because, as President David O. McKay wrote,

> Man is a spiritual being, a soul, and at some period of his life everyone is possessed with an irresistible desire to know his relationship to the Infinite. . . . There is something within him which urges him to rise above himself, to control his environment, to master the body and all things physical and live in a higher and more beautiful world.[14]

Spirituality and the cultivation of spiritual health can have an influence on physical, mental, and emotional health—sometimes in very dramatic ways. Spirituality buffers stress, making us better able to resist and fight disease. A deep sense of spirituality causes a physical relaxation that reduces blood pressure and slows the heart rate. People heal more quickly and completely.

One of the reasons spirituality impacts physical health is that people with a deep sense of spirituality stop focusing on themselves and start focusing on others—an attitude that promotes health in general. As the Savior taught, "He that findeth his life shall lose it: and he that loseth his life for my sake shall find it" (Matthew 10:39).

Because spirituality helps people see life differently and gives greater purpose and meaning to life, people with a deep sense of spirituality are not defeated by crisis. In fact, spirituality helps people interpret crisis as a growth experience. As President Marion G. Romney stated, "I have seen the remorse and despair in the lives of men who, in the hour of trial, have cursed God and died spiritually. And I have seen people rise to great heights from what seemed to be unbearable burdens."[15]

Experienced clinician and educator Paul Pearsall, who founded and directs the Problems of Daily Living Clinic at Detroit's Sinai Hospital, remembers a woman who exemplified spirituality and spiritual health:

> I will never forget her. As she laughed, her hand went to her forehead to brush her hair from her eyes. Purple numbers were tattooed on her wrist. She called them her death marks but said that they had strangely protected and renewed her life during her suffering. She had been tortured, seen her own parents and almost all of her relatives killed, and had lived in the agony, squalor, and starvation of a prison camp for most of the young years of her life. She had every reason to be weak, bitter, sick, and depressed. Instead, she was one of the most joyful, hardy women I have ever met.[16]

Pearsall attributes the woman's health, strength, and resilience to a deep sense of spirituality that helped her find meaning and purpose in life, even in the midst of crisis.

"Thrust a man into prison and bind him with chains," challenged President Brigham Young, "and then let him be filled with the comfort and the glory of eternity, and that prison is a palace to him. . . . When a person is filled with the peace and power of God, all is right with him."[17] Joseph Smith was falsely charged with every kind of evil, thrown into prison, and forced to witness scenes of blasphemy. "But even as he protested these atrocities," said President Marion G. Romney, "his soul expanded as he endured them." At the same time, the Saints were being "ravished and plundered, robbed and driven from their homes, in the dead of winter." To those Saints, Joseph Smith wrote the following from Liberty Jail in March 1839:

> Our circumstances are calculated to awaken our spirits to a sacred remembrance of everything, and we think that yours are also, and that nothing . . . can separate us from the love of God and fellowship one with another; and that every species of wickedness and cruelty practiced upon us will only tend to bind our hearts together and seal them together in love.[18]

Speaking for himself and his fellow prisoners, Joseph Smith wrote, "we are determined to endure tribulation as good soldiers unto the end."[19] Indeed, President Brigham Young observed that the Prophet Joseph Smith was more perfect in thirty-eight years "with the severe tribulation through which he passed" than he would have been in a thousand years without it.[20] In speaking of the Prophet Joseph's triumph over tribulation, Elder Orson F. Whitney remarked that it is "for our development, our purification, our growth, our education and advancement, that we buffet the fierce waves of sorrow and misfortune; and we shall be all the stronger and better when we have swum the flood and stand upon the farther shore."[21]

President Marion G. Romney said, "I have sought the Lord in my own extremities and learned for myself that my soul has made its greatest growth as I have been driven to my knees by adversity and affliction. . . . 'Therefore I take pleasure in infirmities, in reproaches, in necessities, in persecutions, in distresses for Christ's sake: for when I am weak, then am I strong.' (2 Corinthians 12:9-10.)"[22]

"There are those who have met disaster, which almost seems defeat, who have become somewhat soured in their natures," said President David O. McKay, "but if they stop to think, even the adversity which has come to them may prove a means of spiritual uplift. Adversity itself may lead toward and not away from God and spiritual enlightenment; and privation may prove a source of strength if we can but keep the sweetness of mind and spirit."[23]

Elder Neal A. Maxwell asked the probing question, "Do we really want immunity from adversity? Especially when certain kinds of suffering can aid our growth in this life?" To deprive ourselves of adversity, he pointed out, would deprive us of the opportunities for eternal progression—the opportunities we so anticipated in experiencing mortality.[24] And, as Ernest Hemingway so eloquently put it, the world breaks everyone—and some become strongest at the broken places.

In discussing the issue of spirituality and the growth that can come from adversity, Bernie Siegel talks about what he calls "a spiritual flat tire":

> Sometimes adversity and affliction direct you into the proper place so that when you have a flat tire that makes you miss a plane that later crashes, you embrace the tire, bronze it, and hang it over your fireplace as the spiritual flat tire that saved your life. But while you are fixing the tire you are screaming and yelling and getting dirty and mad that you are going to miss your plane. There are many things in life that redirect our lives. So I don't judge things as good, bad, right or wrong. Just sit back and say, "We'll see."[25]

The spirituality that helps people deal with such adversity is an important gift, a talent that must be cultivated. "All men do not come into this world with the same inclination toward or receptiveness of spiritual things," wrote Elder Bruce R. McConkie. "One of the greatest endowments a mortal man can receive is the gift of spirituality, the talent and ability to recognize and cleave unto the truth."[26] On another occasion he added, "The greatest and most important talent or capacity that any of the spirit children of the Father could gain is the talent of spirituality."[27]

How, then, can we develop that talent? It can seem a daunting task. It is easy to become overwhelmed. President Howard W. Hunter taught:

> Part of our difficulty as we strive to acquire spirituality is the feeling that there is much to do and that we are falling far short. Perfection is something yet ahead for every one of us; but we can capitalize on our strengths, begin where

> we are, and seek after the happiness that can be found in pursuing the things of God. . . . The place to begin is here. The time to start is now. The length of our stride need be but one step at a time. God, who has "designed our happiness," will lead us along even as little children, and we will by that process approach perfection.[28]

Elder Dallin H. Oaks wrote:

> We seek spirituality through faith, repentance, and baptism; through forgiveness of one another; through fasting and prayer; through righteous desires and pure thoughts and actions. We seek spirituality through service to our fellowmen; through worship; through feasting on the word of God, in the scriptures and in the teachings of the living prophets. We attain spirituality through making and keeping covenants with the Lord, through conscientiously trying to keep all the commandments of God.[29]

"None of us has attained perfection of the zenith of spiritual growth that is possible in mortality," Elder Dallin H. Oaks continued. "Every person can and must make spiritual progress. The gospel of Jesus Christ is the divine plan for that spiritual growth eternally. . . . With faith in the Lord Jesus Christ and obedience to his gospel, a step at a time improving as we go, pleading for strength, improving our attitudes and our ambitions, we will find ourselves successfully in the fold of the Good Shepherd."[30]

President Howard W. Hunter likened the process of developing spirituality to that of an athlete training for competition as he paraphrased the Apostle Paul's words to the Corinthians: "You know (do you not?) that at the sports all the runners run the race, though only one wins the prize. Like them, run to win! Now every athlete goes into strict training. They do it to win a perishable wreath, but our wreath will last forever. For my part I run with a clear goal before me" (see 1 Corinthians 9:24-26).[31]

In ancient times, President Hunter reminded us, the athletic contest was "the ultimate experience—a hand-to-hand battle to the death." To the Ephesians, Paul detailed what was required for such physical, and spiritual, combat:

> Put on the whole armour of God, that ye may be able to stand against the wiles of the devil.
> For we wrestle not against flesh and blood, but against principalities, against powers, against the rulers of the darkness of this world, against spiritual wickedness in high places.
> Wherefore take unto you the whole armour of God, that ye may be able to withstand in the evil day, and having done all, to stand.
> Stand therefore, having your loins girt about with truth, and having on the breastplate of righteousness;
> And your feet shod with the preparation of the gospel of peace;
> Above all, taking the shield of faith, wherewith ye shall be able to quench all the fiery darts of the wicked.
> And take the helmet of salvation, and the sword of the Spirit, which is the word of God:
> Praying always with all prayer and supplication in the Spirit, and watching thereunto with all perseverance and supplication for all saints. (Ephesians 6:11-18)

The Prophet Joseph Smith did not speak in athletic terms about the struggle to gain spirituality, but he spelled out the time and patience required to gain the prize:

> We consider that God has created man with a mind capable of instruction, and a faculty which may be enlarged in proportion to the heed and diligence given to the light communicated from heaven to the intellect; and that the nearer man approaches perfection, the clearer are his views, and the greater his enjoyments, till he has overcome the evils of his life and lost every desire for sin; and like the ancients, arrives at that point of faith where he is

> wrapped in the power and glory of his Maker, and is caught up to dwell with Him. But we consider that this is a station to which no man ever arrived in a moment.[32]

Tennyson's character, Sir Galahad, claimed, "My strength is as the strength of ten, because my heart is pure." The strength he referred to was not only physical, but spiritual. It was, as Elder Delbert L. Stapley said, "moral strength, the strength that resides in the purity of life, that faces danger, disaster, abuse, false witness, and accusation undaunted; the strength that comes from doing right and living righteously before the Lord."[33]

Finally, we should remember to ask for help in our quest for spirituality, as did Nephi in this stirring prayer:

> O Lord, I have trusted in thee, and I will trust in thee forever. I will not put my trust in the arm of flesh. . . .
>
> Yea, I know that God will give liberally to him that asketh. Yea, my God will give me, if I ask not amiss; therefore I will lift up my voice unto thee, my God, the rock of my righteousness. (2 Nephi 4:33-35.)

END NOTES

1. David O. McKay, *True to the Faith*, comp. by Llewelyn R. McKay (Salt Lake City: Bookcraft, 1966), pp. 244-45.
2. Ezra Taft Benson, *Teachings of Ezra Taft Benson* (Salt Lake City: Bookcraft, 1988), p. 76.
3. Bruce R. McConkie, *Mormon Doctrine,* 2nd edition, revised (Salt Lake City: Bookcraft, 1966), p. 760.
4. Hugh Nibley, *Approaching Zion: Collected Works of Hugh Nibley,* Vol. 9 (Salt Lake City and Provo, Utah: Deseret Book and the Foundation for Ancient Research and Mormon Studies, 1989), p. 281.
5. David O. McKay, *Conference Report* (Salt Lake City: The Church of Jesus Christ of Latter-day Saints, October 1963), pp. 89-90.
6. John Wells, *Conference Report*, October 1933, p. 92.
7. Dallin H. Oaks, *Pure in Heart* (Salt Lake City, Utah: Bookcraft,

1988), p. 112.
8. Larry S. Chapman, "Developing a Useful Perspective on Spiritual Health: Love, Joy, Peace, and Fulfillment," *American Journal of Health Promotion,* Fall 1987, p. 12.
9. Florence Graves, "The High Priest of Healing," *New Age Journal,* May/June 1989, p. 36.
10. Marc Barasch, "The Healing Path: A Soul Approach to Illness," *The Psychology of Health, Immunity, and Disease,* Vol. B, p. 10, in Proceedings of the Sixth International Conference of the National Institute for the Clinical Application of Behavioral Medicine, Hilton Head, S.C., 1994.
11. O. Carl Simonton and Reid Henson, *The Healing Journey* (New York: Bantam Books, 1992), p. 13.
12. Rachel Naomi Remen, "On Defining Spirit," *Noetic Sciences Review,* Autumn 1988, p. 7.
13. Joseph Fielding Smith, *Doctrines of Salvation,* Vol. 1 (Salt Lake City: Bookcraft), p. 52.
14. David O. McKay, *True to the Faith,* comp. by Llewelyn R. McKay (Salt Lake City: Bookcraft, 1966), p. 244.
15. Marion G. Romney, *Conference Report,* October 1969, p. 60.
16. Paul Pearsall, *Super Joy* (New York: Doubleday, 1988), p. 1.
17. Brigham Young, *Discourses of Brigham Young,* selected by John A. Widtsoe (Salt Lake City: Deseret Book, 1941), p. 33.
18. *Documentary History of the Church,* Vol. 3, p. 290.
19. Ibid., p. 294.
20. Truman Madsen, *Eternal Man* (Salt Lake City: Deseret Book, 1966), p. 61.
21. L.G. Otten and C.M. Caldwell, *Sacred Truths of the Doctrine and Covenants,* Vol. 2 (Springville, Utah: LEMB, 1982), p. 302.
22. Marion G. Romney, *Conference Report,* October 1969, p. 60.
23. David O. McKay, *Conference Report,* October 1936, p. 103.
24. Neal A. Maxwell, *All These Things Shall Give Thee Experience* (Salt Lake City: Deseret Book, 1980), pp. 26-27.
25. Florence Graves, "The High Priest of Healing," *New Age Journal,* May/June 1989, p. 32.
26. Bruce R. McConkie, *Mormon Doctrine,* 2nd edition, revised (Salt Lake City: Bookcraft, 1966), p. 761.

27. Bruce R. McConkie, *A New Witness for the Articles of Faith* (Salt Lake City: Deseret Book, 1985), pp. 512-13.
28. Howard W. Hunter, *Conference Report*, April 1979, p. 36.
29. Dallin H. Oaks, *Pure in Heart* (Salt Lake City: Bookcraft, 1988), p. 123.
30. Ibid., pp. 144-45.
31. Howard W. Hunter, "Developing Spirituality," *Ensign,* May 1979, p. 25.
32. *History of the Church,* Vol. 2, p. 8.
33. Delbert L. Stapley, *Conference Report*, October 1967, pp. 74-75.

We need mercy; then let us be merciful. We need charity; let us be charitable. We need forgiveness; let us forgive.

— JOSEPH FIELDING SMITH

CHAPTER

17

The Healing Power of Forgiveness

Scriptural accounts impress upon us the powerful ability to forgive. Stephen, "full of faith and power, did great wonders and miracles" (Acts 6:8) among the people of Jerusalem. At one point, he was transfigured before the Sanhedrin. But the unbelievers who disputed his teachings rose up against him and physically tortured him. Stephen, gazing into the heavens, saw "the glory of God, and Jesus standing on the right hand of God" (Acts 7:55).

Finding no other charge against him, the mobs accused Stephen of blasphemy. They drove him out of the city and stoned him. As he fell to his death, he cried his last words in a loud voice: "Lord, lay not this sin to their charge" (Acts 7:60).

Near the end of his mortal probation, the Prophet Joseph Smith was held prisoner in a dank, cramped cell in Liberty Jail. He had, since kneeling in innocent faith in the Sacred Grove, been stalked and driven from one place to another. His property had been destroyed. He had been covered with boiling tar and studded with colored feathers. He had seen men he loved murdered by the relentless mobs.

Joseph himself described the "dark and blackening deeds" of the mobs "enough to make hell itself shudder, and to stand aghast and pale, and the hands of the very devil to tremble and palsy" (D&C 123:10). Yet from his cell in Liberty Jail he penned a prayer in which he recounted the need to be "full of charity towards all men" (D&C 121:45).

Rather than concentrate on his own difficult situation, he turned his heart and his mind to the Saints. During the few years following his incarceration in Liberty—years of increasing persecution—came some of the most important revelations of this dispensation, among them instructions on baptism for the dead, information about the priesthood, descriptions of the godhead, and teachings about eternal marriage.

As Joseph Smith entered Carthage Jail, facing certain annihilation, he made a simple statement that is stirring in its attitude of forgiveness: "I am going like a lamb to the slaughter; but I am calm as a summer's morning; I have a conscience void of offense towards God, and towards all men" (D&C 135:4). As did Jesus, Joseph prayed, "Father, forgive me my trespasses as I forgive those who trespass against me, for I freely forgive all men."[1]

The ultimate example in forgiveness, as in all else, is provided by the Savior. He had suffered excruciating agony in Gethsemane, which caused him to bleed at every pore. So grave was his suffering that an angel appeared unto him "from heaven, strengthening him" (Luke 22:43). He had been betrayed by one disciple, disavowed by another. He had withstood the mockeries and perversions of an unjust trial. A crown of plaited thorns pierced his head. In his weakness and his pain, he had dragged the heavy cross along the narrow streets until he could carry it no longer and another was "compelled to bear his cross" (Matthew 27:32).

Then he was nailed to the cross, and crucified. A sign was nailed above his head. Those who hung at either side tempted him to save himself; the jeering crowd chose a murderer over the Savior of the world when asked which prisoner should go free. In answer to his parched lips, he was offered vinegar. Only after hours of unrelenting pain did he give up the ghost.

But as the upright cross first bore its holy victim, the Savior was not full of recrimination. Instead, he uttered the most famous prayer of pardon ever offered: "Father, forgive them, for they know not what they do" (Luke 23:34).

Perhaps nowhere in the gospel is the golden rule more evident than with the principle of forgiveness. "For if ye forgive men their trespasses, your heavenly Father will also forgive you," taught Jesus. "But if ye forgive not men their trespasses, neither will your Father forgive your trespasses" (Matthew 6:14-15).

In the gospel according to Mark, the same warning is issued: "But if ye do not forgive, neither will your Father which is in heaven forgive your trespasses. . . . Judge not, and ye shall not be judged: condemn not, and ye shall not be condemned: forgive, and ye shall be forgiven" (Mark 11:26, 37).

When the troubled Alma "poured out his whole soul to God" (Mosiah 26:14), the voice of the Lord spoke to him, promising eternal life. As part of his divine instruction, the Lord told Alma to "forgive one another your trespasses; for verily I say unto you, he that forgiveth not his neighbor's trespasses when he says that he repents, the same hath brought himself under condemnation" (Mosiah 26:31).

So serious is the failure to forgive, in fact, that the person who refuses to forgive a trespass has committed "the greater sin" (D&C 64:9). Our obligation is all-encompassing. "I, the Lord, will forgive whom I will forgive," comes the divine admonition, "but of you it is required to forgive all men" (D&C 64:10).

One of the most classic scriptural accounts of forgiveness involved Peter's query of the Lord, "How oft shall my brother sin against me, and I forgive him?" President David O. McKay gives insight to Peter's probable state of mind that day in Galilee:

> Perhaps Peter had already been required to settle some difficulty between angry men, or, it may be, that he had

> been provoked during a dispute that arose among the disciples as to who was the greatest among them. If some one had taunted him several times . . . , it is quite probable that his patience was exhausted. At any rate, he wanted to know if there is a limit to the number of times a man should forgive his brother. What a lesson Jesus taught this impetuous apostle when he answered, "I say not unto thee, until seven times; but until seventy times seven."[2]

Then, to emphasize the lesson—one Peter would undoubtedly never forget—the Lord related the parable of the unmerciful debtor. A servant owed the king ten thousand talents, an amount equivalent to about $15 million. It was clear the servant had no capability to ever repay the debt. As was the custom, the king demanded that the servant be sold, along with his wife, his children, and all his property.

As a last resort, the servant begged for mercy. If the king would just have patience, the servant promised, he would eventually pay the entire debt. The king was so filled with compassion at the servant's plea that he released him from prison, united him with his family, returned his property, and forgave him the debt.

The servant, relieved, went on his way. That should have been the end of it, but it wasn't. Soon the servant ran into a fellow-servant who owed him a hundred pence—*a million times less than the servant had owed the king.* But did he look the other direction? No. He grabbed the fellow-servant by the neck, started choking him, and demanded payment on the spot.

Of course, the fellow-servant couldn't pay the debt. He begged for mercy, much as the servant himself had done. But his pleadings fell on deaf ears. The servant had him thrown into prison until he could pay the hundred pence.

News of the incident filtered back to the king, and the king sent for the servant. "O thou wicked servant, I forgave thee all that debt, because thou desiredst me," the king said. "Shouldest not thou also have had compassion on thy fellowservant, even as I had pity on thee?" (Matthew 18:33).

In his righteous anger at the servant, the king restored the debt of ten thousand talents. Then the king threw the servant to the "tormentors" until the entire debt was paid.

Concluding the parable, the Lord told Peter, and all of us, "So likewise shall my heavenly Father do also unto you, if ye from your hearts forgive not every one his brother their trespasses" (Matthew 18: 35).

President Spencer W. Kimball likened us to the pleading servant, begging for his debt to be canceled: "A pleading sinner must also forgive all people of all offenses committed against himself. The Lord is under no obligation to forgive us unless our hearts are fully purged of all hate, bitterness, and accusations against all others."[3]

What about those who do not seem to merit our forgiveness? "A common idea is that the offender must apologize and humble himself to the dust before forgiveness is required," President Kimball taught. Such is not the case. The Lord makes clear our obligation to forgive, regardless of the offender's attitude.[4] Our response when we are offended, misunderstood, unfairly treated, falsely accused, or hurt by those we love, taught Elder Marion D. Hanks, "may well determine the nature and quality of our lives, here and eternally."[5]

The Lord himself provided an example of unsolicited—and probably undeserved—forgiveness as he hung on the cross at Golgotha. "Without their asking for forgiveness and without any sign of repentance, and while they were still in their murderous passion, he found it in his heart to forgive them," wrote President Spencer W. Kimball of the Savior's declaration. "He did not wait till his crucifiers should have a change of heart; but he forgave them while they were yet crimson with his life's blood."[6]

Of the need to forgive regardless of another's state of mind, Elder Neal A. Maxwell wrote, "I have learned by sad experience that there is no expiation in retaliation; vengeance not only prolongs conflict, but also deepens and widens it."[7]

Why is forgiveness so important to the Lord? Why does the Lord ask that we forgive, that we return good for evil? One reason may be so we can be blessed by the healing power of forgiveness. As President Spencer W. Kimball taught, your failure to forgive doesn't injure the other person, "but the hate and bitterness canker your unforgiving heart. . . . Bitterness injures the one who carries it—it hardens and shrivels and cankers."[8] On another occasion, he reminded us that the hated one generally "does not even know how bitter is the animosity leveled against him. He may sleep at night and enjoy a reasonable peace, but the one who hates estranges himself from good folk, shrivels his heart, dwarfs his soul, makes of himself an unhappy pygmy."[9]

Indeed, forgiveness has been defined as a "process of healing." What some have also called "the first step on the pathway to healing," forgiveness enables one to banish resentment. It is, as Dr. Joan Borysenko put it, "accepting the core of every human being as the same as yourself and giving them the gift of not judging them."[10]

According to psychotherapist Robin Casarjian, founder and director of the Lionheart Foundation, forgiveness is "a relationship with life that frees the forgiver from the psychological bondage of chronic fear, hostility, anger, and unhealthy guilt."[11] Forgiveness, she says, is an attitude that implies that you are willing to accept responsibility for your perceptions, realizing that *"your perceptions are a choice and not an objective fact."*

Forgiveness isn't easy; in fact, most people who responded to one poll said they had great difficulty forgiving others. Speaking of forgiveness, President Spencer W. Kimball said:

> Hard to do? Of course. The Lord never promised an easy road, nor a simple gospel, nor low standards, nor a low norm. The price is high, but the goods attained are worth all they cost. The Lord himself turned the other cheek; he suffered himself to be buffeted and beaten without remonstrance; he suffered every indignity and yet spoke no word of condemnation. And his question to all of us is: "Therefore, what manner of men ought ye to be?" And his answer to us is: "Even as I am." (3 Nephi 27:27.)[12]

Forgiveness is *not* condoning negative, inappropriate behavior, your own or someone else's, says Casarjian. It is also not "pretending everything is just fine when you feel it isn't, or assuming an attitude of superiority or self-righteousness." Instead, she says, it is a "decision to see beyond the limits of another's personality; to be willing to accept responsibility for your own perceptions; to shift your perceptions repeatedly; and to gradually transform yourself from being a helpless victim of your circumstances to being a powerful and loving co-creator of your reality."[13]

Forgiveness—and the failure to forgive—affects not only the mind and the spirit, but the body. When we don't forgive, the body pumps "high-voltage" chemicals into the bloodstream. They include chemicals like adrenaline, noradrenaline, and cortisone.[14] As these chemicals build up in the bloodstream, the body literally becomes a rapidly ticking time bomb. The heart pounds in the chest like a sledgehammer. The muscles of the neck and shoulders gradually tighten. Abdominal pains develop.

If the situation continues unchecked, the body pays the price. The person who fails to forgive becomes a candidate for gastric ulcers, gastritis, irritable bowel syndrome, and tension/vascular headache.[15]

Forgiveness reverses the process. Anger and resentment dissolve. The body stops pouring high-voltage chemicals into the bloodstream. The heart rate drops. Muscle tension eases. The healing begins.

Without forgiveness, we are constrained; when we forgive, we become free. Internist and cardiologist Dr. Bruno Cortis compares the burden of failing to forgive to that of carrying a heavy object:

> I often imagine some of my patients walking along holding a heavy object, like a chair. As they walk, they can choose which path to take, so they are seemingly free. However, in reality they are not free, because they are carrying this extra weight, which becomes heavier and heavier with each step. It's only when they put down this load that they regain their freedom.

> That imaginary weight is, of course, the burden of the past: resentments, angers, and guilts that we have heaped upon ourselves. To free ourselves from this oppression, we must learn to forgive ourselves and others.[16]

One of the greatest examples of the healing power of forgiveness can be found in nature. As one author put it:

> Nature always forgives. Nature is the great giver and the great forgiver. Should you cut your hand with a sharp knife, the forces of nature set about immediately to repair the damage. It was a mistake to cut your hand, but nature does not withhold the repairing of the wound. Nature immediately forgives and starts at once to make repairs. If you eat food that does not agree with you and you have indigestion, nature immediately starts to repair the damage. Although it was a mistake to eat the wrong food, you do not have to go through the rest of your life with indigestion. Nature even repairs the ravages of the battlefield by covering it with grass and flowers. [No one] can go forward if he is tied to the past. No one can think straight and efficiently if his mind is cluttered up with thoughts of hate or memories of hurts and mistakes; hence the necessity of forgiving so that we can love ourselves, our neighbor, and God.[17]

At the conclusion of the October 1902 General Conference of the Church, President Joseph F. Smith told the Saints gathered in the Salt Lake Tabernacle:

> We ought to say in our hearts, let God judge between me and thee, but as for me, I will forgive. . . . Dismiss envy and hatred from your hearts; dismiss the feeling of unforgiveness; and cultivate in your souls that spirit of Christ which cried out upon the cross, "Father, forgive them, for they know not what they do." . . . The man who has that spirit in his heart and keeps it there . . . will always be at peace with himself, at peace with his neighbors, and at peace with God.[18]

In fact, we are commanded to forgive all men (see D&C 64:10). President Spencer W. Kimball said that "to be in the right we must forgive, and we must do so *without regard to whether or not our antagonist repents,* or how sincere is his transformation, or whether or not he asks our forgiveness."[19]

To us, the charge is to forgive others and, equally as important, to forgive ourselves. President Gordon B. Hinckley reminded us of the words of the Master Healer, who commanded us to love our enemies, to bless those that curse us, to do good to those that hate us, and to pray for those that despitefully use us (see Matthew 5:44). Then President Hinckley taught:

> Most of us have not reached that stage of compassion and love and forgiveness. It is not easy. It requires a self-discipline almost greater than we are capable of. But as we try, we come to know that there is a resource of healing, that there is a mighty power of healing in Christ, and that if we are to be His true servants we must not only exercise that healing power in behalf of others, but, perhaps more importantly, inwardly.[20]

The rewards of such forgiveness can include physical well-being as well as spiritual well-being. It can also include unmeasured joy, as foretold by President Spencer W. Kimball:

> If we would sue for peace, taking the initiative in settling differences—if we would forgive and forget with all our hearts—if we would cleanse our own souls of sin, bitterness, and guilt before we cast a stone of accusation at others—if we would forgive all real or fancied offenses before we asked forgiveness for our own sins—if we would pay our own debts, large or small, before we pressed our debtors—if we would manage to clear our own eyes of the blinding beams before we magnified the motes in the eyes of others—what a glorious world this would be! Divorce would be reduced to a minimum; courts would be freed from disgusting routines; family life would be heavenly; the

> building of the kingdom would go forward at an accelerated pace; and that peace which passeth all understanding would bring to us all a joy and happiness that has hardly "entered into the heart of man."[21]

END NOTES

1. Joseph Fielding Smith, ed., *Teachings of the Prophet Joseph Smith* (Salt Lake City: Deseret Book, 1938), p. 312.
2. David O. McKay, *Ancient Apostles* (Salt Lake City: Deseret Sunday School Union, 1918), p. 53.
3. Spencer W. Kimball, *The Teachings of Spencer W. Kimball*, comp. by Edward L. Kimball (Salt Lake City: Bookcraft, 1982), p. 86.
4. Spencer W. Kimball, *The Miracle of Forgiveness* (Salt Lake City: Bookcraft, 1969), p. 282.
5. Marion D. Hanks, *Conference Report*, October 1973, p. 15.
6. Spencer W. Kimball, *Faith Precedes the Miracle* (Salt Lake City: Deseret Book, 1972), p. 194.
7. Neal A. Maxwell, *Of One Heart: The Glory of the City of Enoch* (Salt Lake City: Deseret Book, 1975), p. 41.
8. Spencer W. Kimball, *The Teachings of Spencer W. Kimball*, comp. by Edward L. Kimball (Salt Lake City: Bookcraft, 1982), p. 103.
9. Spencer W. Kimball, *The Miracle of Forgiveness* (Salt Lake City: Bookcraft, 1969), p. 272.
10. Joan Borysenko, *Minding the Body, Mending the Mind* (Reading, Mass.: Addison-Wesley Publishing Company, Inc., 1987), p. 176.
11. Robin Casarjian, "Forgiveness: An Essential Component in Health and Healing," in Proceedings of the Fourth National Conference on the Psychology of Health, Immunity, and Disease, published by the National Institute for the Clinical Application of Behavioral Medicine, Boston, Mass, 1992.
12. Spencer W. Kimball, *The Teachings of Spencer W. Kimball,* comp. by Edward L. Kimball (Salt Lake City: Bookcraft, 1982), p. 102.
13. Robin Casarjian, "Forgiveness: An Essential Component in Health and Healing," in Proceedings of the Fourth National Conference on the Psychology of Health, Immunity, and Disease, published by the National Institute for the Clinical Application of Behavioral Medicine, Boston, Mass, 1992.

14. Arnold Fox and Barry Fox, *Wake Up! You're Alive* (Deerfield Beach, Fla.: Health Communications, Inc., 1988), p. 102.
15. Ibid.
16. Bruno Cortis, *Heart and Soul* (New York: Villard Books, 1995), pp. 87-88.
17. Dan Custer, *The Miracle of Mind Power* (Englewood Cliffs, N.J.: Prentice-Hall, Inc., 1960), p. 92.
18. Joseph Fielding Smith, *Gospel Doctrine,* comp. by John A. Widtsoe (Salt Lake City: Deseret Book, 1919), p. 255.
19. Spencer W. Kimball, *The Miracle of Forgiveness* (Salt Lake City: Bookcraft, 1969), p. 283.
20. Gordon B. Hinckley, *Conference Report,* October 1988, p. 68.
21. Spencer W. Kimball, *Faith Precedes the Miracle* (Salt Lake City: Deseret Book, 1972), pp. 195-96.

Prayer will bring solace and comfort. It has healed sickness, comforted those distressed, and has continued the faithful in paths of righteousness. The value of a man is evidenced in part by the dust on his knees.

— Ezra Taft Benson

CHAPTER

18

The Power of Prayer

One of the most compelling examples of prayer is provided by the repentant Enos, who went deep into the forest to plead with his Father in Heaven for a remission of his sins. In one of the briefest yet most powerful sections of the Book of Mormon, Enos gives a graphic account of "the wrestle which I had before God" (Enos 1:2).

Enos was "traveling a path he had never walked before," wrote President Spencer W. Kimball. "He was reaching, knocking, asking, pleading; he was being born again. He was seeing the pleasant valleys across the barren wastes. He was searching his soul. He might have lived all his life in a weed patch, but now he envisioned a watered garden."[1]

Enos had been stirred by the admonitions of his father, and he hungered for a life of righteousness. The memory of previous deeds seared his soul; he longed, as President Kimball wrote, "to bury the old man of sin, to resurrect the new man of faith, of godliness."

And so, writes Enos, "I kneeled down before my Maker, and I cried unto him in mighty prayer and supplication for mine own soul" (Enos 1:4). The prayer that escaped his lips was vocal and powerful. It was, said President Kimball, "a heart-wrenching, imploring, begging and pleading." Enos had come to realize that he could not enter the kingdom of God in his current state—that "there must be a purging, a new heart in a new man. He knew it was not a small thing to change hearts and minds."[2]

And so, writes Enos, "all the day long did I cry unto him; yea, and when the night came I did still raise my voice high that it reached the heavens" (Enos 1:4). How many of us have prayed all day and into the night? Have many of us have prayed and wept for even an entire hour? President Kimball gave a glimpse of the intensity of Enos's petition:

> Here is no casual prayer; no worn phrases; no momentary appeal by silent lips. All the day long, with seconds turning into minutes, and minutes into hours and hours. But when the sun had set, relief had still not come, for repentance is not a single act nor forgiveness an unearned gift. So precious to him was communication with and approval of his Redeemer that his determined soul pressed on without ceasing. Could the Redeemer resist such determined imploring?[3]

No. Enos's mighty efforts at last brought the sought-after cleansing, the absolute change of heart and mind. The voice of the Lord came into his mind, saying, "thy sins are forgiven thee, and thou shalt be blessed. . . . Because of thy faith in Christ . . . I will grant unto thee according to thy desires." (Enos 1:5, 8, 12).

Enos achieved what President Spencer W. Kimball called "the ultimate object of all prayer": to "bring men closer to God, to give them a new birth, to make them heirs of his kingdom."[4]

We are reminded of other singular prayers that have changed the course of mankind. "Fervent prayer on the part of a young fourteen-year-old boy in New York State in 1820 started a chain of events that is literally changing the lives of millions of people today," taught President Ezra Taft Benson. "The direct result of this prayer has brought a positive understanding of the being of

God the Father and His Son, Jesus Christ. It has caused the uncovering of ancient histories which contain divine truths that if obeyed will lead directly to the eventual exaltation of man."[5]

Great men and women have always recognized the strength that comes from prayer. "Washington at Valley Forge, Lincoln before Gettysburg, Eisenhower on D-Day, Jesus at Gethsemane and at Golgotha—all these have prayed."[6] Modern-day revelation advises us to "Pray always, that you may come off conqueror" (D&C 10:5).

Prayer gives us new birth and brings us close to God. As Alma taught, "All mankind . . . must be born again; yea, born of God, changed from their carnal and fallen state, to a state of righteousness, being redeemed of God, becoming his sons and daughters; . . . And thus they become new creatures; and unless they do this, they can in nowise inherit the kingdom of God" (Mosiah 27:25-26). Prayer is our way of communicating with our Heavenly Father, of becoming born again.

Our Father in Heaven has invited us to counsel with him—to pray to him. Part and parcel of that invitation is the bid to tap unseen powers, to solicit his help. Instead of promising freedom from adversity and affliction, the Lord "has given us the avenue of communication known as prayer, whereby we might humble ourselves and seek his help and divine guidance," wrote President Spencer W. Kimball.[7]

The Savior testified, "Behold, I stand at the door, and knock: if any man hear my voice, and open the door, I will come in to him, and will sup with him, and he with me" (Revelation 3:20). As President Kimball wrote, that promise "is made to everyone. There is no discrimination, no favored few, but the Lord has not promised to crash the door. He stands and knocks. . . . He never retreats. But he will never force himself upon us. If our distance from him increases, it is we who have moved and not the Lord."[8]

A part of spiritual maturity occurs when we acknowledge that there is an unseen source of power and truth, a "profound realization that man does not stand alone." As President Howard W.

Hunter taught, "no promise in life is more reassuring than that promise of divine assistance and spiritual guidance in times of need. It is a gift freely given from heaven, a gift that we need from our earliest youth through the very latest days of our lives."[9] There are, as President Ezra Taft Benson taught, "hidden treasures of knowledge for him who asks in faith, nothing wavering. Such has been the fervent declaration of the world's truly great leaders in all ages of recorded history. Prayer has always been an unfailing source of strength and inspiration."[10]

Prayer signals our humble dependency on the Lord for help and strength, as expressed in Nephi's stirring supplication: "O Lord, I have trusted in thee, and I will trust in thee forever. . . . Yea, I know that God will give liberally to him that asketh. Yea, my God will give me, if I ask not amiss; therefore I will lift up my voice unto thee; yea, I will cry unto thee, my God, the rock of my righteousness" (2 Nephi 4:33-35).

For us as Latter-day Saints, prayer is not an optional activity; it is basic to our faith. President Brigham Young observed, "Were I to draw a distinction in all the duties that are required of the children of men, from first to last, I would place first and foremost the duty of seeking unto the Lord our God until we open the path of communication from heaven to earth—from God to our own souls."[11]

We have been commanded to "pray vocally as well as in thy heart; yea, before the world as well as in secret, in public as well as in private" (D&C 19:28). We have been commanded, too, to teach our children "to pray, and to walk uprightly before the Lord" (D&C 68:28).

In all its simplicity, prayer can be a deep and soul-satisfying experience. Prayer, wrote Elder Neal A. Maxwell, "is a marvelous process that pierces the veil, and, therefore, requires much faith and persistence on our part; this is so precisely because prayer is that point where the agency of man meets the omniscience of God, and it is where time melts as it touches eternity," a process that exceeds our limited comprehension.[12]

Prayer signals a commitment to a set of moral and ethical values; it is a signpost of spirituality, and is at the core of most spiritual experiences. Though mortals have been praying for thousands of years, points out Elder Neal A. Maxwell, "prayer is not something we can clinically diagnose and dissect, giving ready answers for every question about every dimension of this great process."[13] What we *can* do is examine the effects of prayer.

Obviously, prayer exerts tremendous spiritual power. We know that prayer can precipitate miracles: the miracle of forgiveness, the miracle of healing, the miracle of a change of heart. In addition to what prayer does for the soul, though, we know that prayer also has powerful physical benefits. When we pray, we are in a state of relaxed alertness, peace, joy, contentment, and emotional release. During prayer, we empty the mind, yet we receive direction. Part of the magnetism of prayer comes from our own belief, our own faith: the powerful suggestion that prayer will work, that something will happen.[14]

One of the most compelling reasons behind the physical benefits of prayer is its subtle peace and quiet effect. Prayer involves solitude, which is *not* the same as loneliness. As President Spencer W. Kimball told a Brigham Young University audience, "Solitude is rich and profitable. When we pray alone with God, we shed all sham and pretense, all hypocrisy and arrogance."[15]

Dr. Herbert Benson, associate professor of medicine at the Harvard Medical School and chief of the Section on Behavioral Medicine at the New England Deaconess Hospital, has focused the last two decades of his clinical work on what he calls "the relaxation response." The relaxation response is the body's ability to enter a "scientifically definable state" of relaxation. Changes occur in the body during the relaxation response: metabolism slows down, blood pressure drops, breathing slows, heart rate drops, and even the brain waves are less active.[16]

What does that have to do with prayer? According to Benson, the relaxation response, with all its physiological benefits, has most often and effectively been elicited through prayer.[17] Most of the physical benefits of prayer can be traced to what researchers call "meditative" prayer: being still, knowing that God is God. In his own practice, as he has struggled to teach patients the relaxation response, Benson has watched the great physical results of prayer. He has written extensively of those results. In one woman, crippling chest pain was resolved. In another, life-threatening high blood pressure dropped.

The relaxation response is not the only way prayer helps buffer the effects of stress. Prayer helps us meditate, which also relieves stress. University of Utah researcher N. Lee Smith says that when people pray, "they're focusing on their deepest values and drawing on spiritual power that develops a sense of connectedness and also develops hope. And that has been known to affect medical outcomes. The mind has the ability to heal in ways that are largely unexplainable."

There's also a direct and obvious way that prayer helps relieve stress. Elder Russell M. Nelson speaks of the "sweet serenity" found in fervent prayer and in acceptance of the Savior's invitation to cast our burdens upon him. "As our burdens are shared with Him," Elder Nelson affirms, "they do become lighter."[18]

When we pray for ourselves, says internist and prayer research pioneer Dr. Larry Dossey, things happen that influence the body:

> You think positively. And positive thoughts aren't confined to your brain. They set in motion a chain of events that has been defined physiologically. We know that expectation and suggestion achieve a lot of fabulous changes in the immune system and probably every other organ in the body.
>
> When you get into a meditative, prayer-like, contemplative frame of mind, the metabolism slows down, the immune system is refreshed, blood pressure and heart rates subside, blood lactate levels fall, and oxygen consumption and carbon dioxide production are diminished. A lot of changes happen, the result of which is that the body becomes healthier. . . .
>
> But most people probably aren't interested in that level. They want to know, "When I pray, does it work or not?" I

> think that if you look at the evidence, you can resoundingly say, "Yup! This has a healthful effect and here's the laboratory proof."[19]

Obviously, praying benefits the person who prays. But can the prayer of one person benefit another? Faithful saints have seen the evidence of it countless times, and during the last decade, science has found evidence of it as well. One chemist, anxious to find out whether the benefits of prayer were simply due to the power of suggestion, did research on subjects that couldn't think for themselves: plants. If prayer worked on plants, he reasoned, there must be some power connected to prayer—something beyond the simple explanation that a human mind believed, and therefore experienced success.

For his experiment, he ran a series of seven hundred tests. A total of 156 people were asked to pray for a randomly selected group of seeds and seedlings. In all, the tests involved more than 2,700 plants. All the growing conditions were exactly the same, but the plants that were prayed for reaped a 52.71 percent advantage in growth.[20]

In a separate study, researchers wanted to know if the same thing would hold true if prayers were uttered from a distance. They asked a group of people to pray for some randomly selected rye grass in a town six hundred miles away. The rye grass that was prayed for showed "remarkable" growth when compared to the growth of the rest of the grass.[21]

Not only plants benefit from prayer. We have seen, and science has confirmed, its powerful impact on people—even those who don't know prayers are being offered in their behalf. In one fascinating study, San Francisco cardiologist Randy Byrd arranged for a group of people around the country to pray daily for 192 coronary care unit patients at San Francisco General Hospital. The patients were chosen at random from a group of 393 coronary patients in the hospital's unit. They were not told that they were part of a study. Nor were they told that anyone was praying for them.

Every day, each person in the group of 192 had from five to seven people praying for him or her. The people who did the praying were given the name of the patient, the patient's diagnosis, a description of the patient's condition, and other relevant facts. They were asked to pray for "beneficial healing and a quick recovery" of each person. The other 201 patients in the coronary care unit had no one in the network praying for them. The study went on for ten months.

The people in the two groups were similar in health condition, age, and other factors. But when Byrd analyzed the data from the study, even he was surprised. The patients who were prayed for were five times less likely to need antibiotics and three times less likely to develop complications than those who were not prayed for.

After studying the experiment, Byrd proclaimed that prayer is "effective and beneficial" in the clinical treatment of patients.[22] Dr. Larry Dossey, after scrutinizing the results of the study, proclaimed that it was "as if the prayed-for group had been given some sort of miracle drug."[23]

How do the scientists explain what happens when one person prays for another? They can't, because it can't be explained on a scientific level. Though the explanation is inconceivable, says Dr. Dossey, "we have occasions in science to acknowledge a phenomenon and to honor its existence without even having a theory and an understanding about how it happens. I think we will acknowledge that many so-called miracles occur without a full understanding of *why*."[24]

A number of physicians have pointed out that prayer, as an expression of spirituality, can work in concert with medical treatment to bring about physiological changes and recoveries. Francis McNutt, director of the Christian Healing Ministries, echoed that sentiment:

> In no way do I conceive prayer for healing as a negation of the need for doctors, nurses, counselors, psychiatrists, or pharmacists. God works in all these ways to heal the sick; the ideal is a team effort to get the sick well through every possible means.[25]

Arthur Kennel, assistant professor of medicine at Mayo Medical School in Rochester, Minnesota, says, "I pray for my own patients, and I feel my prayers benefit them." John Merriman, former professor of medicine and now the chief of staff at Tulsa's Doctors Medical Center, reacted to the San Francisco study without surprise, saying, "I believe that patients who are named in prayer do better."[26]

Those physicians are not alone. In a nationwide poll asking doctors whether they feel patients benefit from prayer and whether they themselves pray for patients, the results favored prayer. Half of the doctors questioned believe prayer helps patients; two-thirds said they pray for their patients.[27]

Commenting on the study, Dr. Lawrence Dorman, an internist from Independence, Missouri, said, "Prayer can be a very powerful tool in helping patients. Many get off their medication much earlier than expected because family members have been praying for them." Nebraska family practitioner Dr. Marlin Bauhard commented, "I've seen recoveries that could only have happened as a result of God."[28]

How can we make our own petitions more effective to more certainly reap the benefits of prayer for ourselves and others? What manner of men and women ought we to be? Even as the Savior is, an answer that brings us to our knees in prayer. "Our great example in prayer is our Lord and Master Jesus Christ," said President Ezra Taft Benson, "who knew that only through constant supplication and obedience would God the Father manifest His will and release the power for its attainment through man."[29]

To the extent that we stray from the example given us by the Savior, we fail in our individual battles. But, President Benson assured us, "we are not without His help. Again and again He told His disciples, and all of us, 'Let not your heart be troubled. . . . If ye shall ask any thing in my name, I will do it. I will not leave you comfortless. . . . Peace I leave with you, my peace I give unto you.' (John 14:1, 14, 18, 27.)"[30] President Benson continued:

> We feel His comforting Spirit in the sweet prayer of a child and the quiet abiding faith of all who have let His gospel permeate their lives. What a priceless gift it is that we can know Him through our own prayers and through the sacred and solemn testimonies of those who have seen Him, known Him, felt His presence.
>
> Will you value and take advantage of the opportunity to tap these unseen but very real spiritual powers? Will you be able to affirm the solemn declaration of an illustrious past president of one of America's leading universities, who has counseled: "Men who search out truth are prayerful. They stand with uncovered heads before the unknown. They know their own insignificance before the eternal fount of knowledge. . . . Manly men who really love truth are proud to pray to God for help and guidance. They get down on their knees. . . . To win knowledge of the unseen, to obtain a testimony of truth, one must pray without ceasing. It must be the first and last act of the day."[31]

A first step involves preparing ourselves to pray, and that involves deep humility. As Alma counseled, "blessed are they who humble themselves without being compelled to be humble" (Alma 32:16). While humility is required for prayer, it is through prayer that we develop humility. President Spencer W. Kimball taught, "How does one get humble? To me, one must constantly be reminded of his dependence. On whom dependent? On the Lord. How remind one's self? By real, constant, worshipful, grateful prayer."[32]

President Joseph F. Smith said:

> It is not such a difficult thing to learn how to pray. It is not the words we use particularly that constitute prayer. . . . True, faithful, earnest prayer consists more in the feeling that rises from the heart and from the inward desire of our spirits to supplicate the Lord in humility and in faith, that we may receive his blessings. It matters not how simple the words may be, if our desires are genuine and we come before the Lord with a broken heart and contrite spirit.[33]

President David O. McKay added to humility a list of other virtues essential to effective prayer: faith, reverence, sincerity, and loyalty. "A belief in God brings peace to the soul," he wrote. "An assurance that God is our Father, into whose presence we can go for comfort and guidance, is a never-failing source of comfort."[34]

As we kneel, we abolish fear from our hearts and place our trust in Him. "There is no place for fear among men and women who place their trust in the Almighty, who do not hesitate to humble themselves in seeking divine guidance through prayer," emphasized President Ezra Taft Benson. "Though persecutions arise, though reverses come, in prayer we can find assurance, for God will speak peace to the soul."[35]

Part of preparing for prayer includes developing Christ-like attributes in our relationships with others. As he wrapped up his moving sermon on prayer to the apostate Zoramites, Amulek warned:

> For after ye have done all these things, if ye turn away the needy, and the naked, and visit not the sick and afflicted, and impart of your substance, if ye have, to those who stand in need—I say unto you, if ye do not any of these things, behold, your prayer is in vain, and availeth you nothing, and ye are as hypocrites who do deny the faith.
>
> Therefore, if ye do not remember to be charitable, ye are as dross, which the refiners do cast out, (it being of no worth). (Alma 34:28-29.)

Much must go into preparing ourselves for prayer, because we stand to gain so much. As Elder Neal A. Maxwell wrote:

> The door to the vault of the treasures of heaven cannot be opened casually any more than the powers of heaven can be controlled except by righteous principles. The vault door has a combination lock: one tumbler falls when faith is present; another as a result of personal righteousness; the final one only when what is petitioned for is (in the judgment of a perfect and loving Father) right for the petitioner and expedient in the judgment of God. Were it not so, we

> would be spoiled and ineffectual children. Our eternal security depends on the security of that vault. If the tumblers fell too easily, so would we.[36]

Next comes the task of finding a place free from distraction, a place where we can pray in secret. In teaching the Nephites about prayer, Jesus admonished:

> And when thou prayest thou shalt not do as the hypocrites, for they love to pray, standing in the synagogues and in the corners of the streets, that they may be seen of men. Verily I say unto you, they have their reward.
>
> But thou, when thou prayest, enter into thy closet, and when thou hast shut thy door, pray to thy Father who is in secret; and thy Father, who seeth in secret, shall reward thee openly. (3 Nephi 13:5-6.)

In a similar vein, Amulek taught that we should pour out our souls in prayer in our closets, in our secret places, and in our wilderness (see Alma 34:28). Examples of such prayerful solitude are plentiful:

> The Savior found His mountains and slipped away to pray. Paul, the great apostle, could not seem to get into the spirit of his new calling until he had found cleansing solitude down in Arabia: for purification; for repentance; for forgiveness, to break the seal of worldly covering, to shed his film, his skintight suit of worldliness. He went into solitude a worldly man and came out cleansed, prepared, regenerated. He was born of water in a Damascus river and of the spirit in an Arabian solitude. Enos found himself in solitary places to commune in forest vastnesses, with only ears of beasts to hear. Moriancumur went to the mountain top to get the Lord to touch the stones to light their way. And Nephi learned to build a ship through communication with his Lord on a mountain far from human ears. Joseph found his solitude in the grove with only birds and trees and God to listen to his prayer.[37]

Prayer should be intensely personal, an effort to talk, one on one, with our Father in Heaven. President David O. McKay reminded us that we can't have an effective prayer "without visualizing and feeling a personal God." President Ezra Taft Benson asked:

> When you pray—when you talk to your Heavenly Father—do you really talk out your problems with Him? Do you let Him know your feelings, your doubts, your insecurities, your joys, your deepest desires? Or is prayer merely a habitual expression with the same words and phrases? Do you ponder what you really mean to say? Do you take time to listen to the promptings of the Spirit? Answers to prayer come most often by a still voice and are discerned by our deepest, innermost feelings. . . . You can know the will of God concerning yourselves if you will take the time to pray and to listen.[38]

In our petitioning, we sometimes too quickly ask for more blessings when we have failed to express real gratitude for blessings already granted. Elder Neal A. Maxwell compares this tendency to being in a stalled car. "Someone gives us a shove, and we are so busy taking advantage of the shove—getting our car working again—that, at most, we thank our benefactor with a wave of the hand or a honk." Blessings from our Father deserve so much more; if we wish to "deepen our relationship with God, there must be time for two-way communication. We are better askers than listeners."[39]

If we seek two-way communication, we must contribute our half. In a sermon to students at Brigham Young University, President Spencer W. Kimball pondered what happens when it seems prayers are not answered. Perhaps, he said, it is because we do not understand. There may be no vibration because our ears do not perceive it. God may not speak, because our ears are closed. He may not appear, because our eyes are leaden. "Some people hear a noise," he said. "Others think it thunders, while others hear and understand the voice of God and see him personally."[40]

It is our responsibility, said Bishop H. Burke Peterson, to listen. Of that responsibility, he taught:

> Listening is an essential part of praying. Answers from the Lord come quietly—ever so quietly. In fact, few hear his answers audibly with their ears. We must be listening so carefully or we will never recognize them. Most answers from the Lord are felt in our heart as a warm comfortable expression, or they may come as thoughts to our mind. They come to those who are prepared and who are patient.[41]

Elder Boyd K. Packer emphasized the importance of *learning* to listen by relating the story of John Burroughs, a naturalist, who was walking through a crowded city park one summer evening. Suddenly, above the chaos of the city, he heard the song of a bird. He stopped and listened—but those who were with him did not hear. "It is difficult to separate from all the sounds of city traffic the song of a bird," he taught. "But you can hear it. You can hear it plainly if you train yourself to listen for it." It is the same, he said, with answers to prayer—and those answers may come in a variety of ways. "Some answers will come from reading the scriptures, some from hearing speakers," he said. "And, occasionally, when it is important, some will come by very direct and powerful inspiration. The promptings will be clear and unmistakable."[42]

What of prayers that, despite our personal effort, go unanswered? Of those prayers, President Spencer W. Kimball taught:

> Faith must be tested. Some become bitter when oft-repeated prayers seem unanswered. Some lose faith and turn sour when solemn administrations by holy men seem to be ignored and no restoration seems to come from repeated prayer circles. But if all the sick were healed, if all the righteous were protected and the wicked destroyed, the whole program of the Father would be annulled and the basic principle of the gospel, free agency, would be ended. . . .

> If pain and sorrow and total punishment immediately followed the doing of evil, no soul would repeat a misdeed. If joy and peace and rewards were instantaneously given the doer of good, there could be no evil—all would do good, and not because of the rightness of doing good. There would be no test of strength, no development of character, no growth of powers, no free agency. . . . There would also be an absence of joy, success, resurrection, eternal life, and godhood.[43]

Worse yet, what if the answer comes, but it is not the answer we sought? Much of prayer is petitioning, but it also involves tutoring. Elder Neal A. Maxwell confirms that prayer must involve "the process of first discovering, rather than requesting, the will of our Father in heaven and then aligning ourselves therewith."[44]

"If I could wish for anyone a priceless gift," wrote Ezra Taft Benson, "it would not be wealth, profound wisdom, or the honors of men. I would rather pass on the key to inner strength and security which my father gave to me when he advised, 'Receive [God's] aid through prayer.'"[45]

Prayer costs nothing more than our own effort, yet it provides the greatest return of any possible investment. As President Ezra Taft Benson counseled:

> Prayer will help you understand the apparent conflicts in life—to know that God lives, that life is eternal. He who is able to avail himself of this blessing in life is free as the boundless universe. He unlocks the doors to the storehouse of all knowledge and power. . . .
>
> If we would advance in holiness—increase in favor with God—nothing can take the place of prayer. And so I adjure you to give prayer—daily prayer, secret prayer—a foremost place in your lives. Let no day pass without it. . . .
>
> Man does not stand alone, or, at least, he need not stand alone. Prayer will open doors; prayer will remove barriers; prayer will ease pressures; prayer will give inner peace and comfort during times of strain and stress and difficulty. Thank God for prayer.[46]

END NOTES

1. This and the following from Spencer W. Kimball, *Faith Precedes the Miracle* (Salt Lake City: Deseret Book, 1972), p. 210.
2. Ibid., p. 211.
3. Ibid.
4. Ibid., p. 212.
5. Ezra Taft Benson, *Teachings of Ezra Taft Benson* (Salt Lake City: Bookcraft, 1988), p. 422.
6. Ibid., p. 429.
7. Spencer W. Kimball, *The Teachings of Spencer W. Kimball,* comp. by Edward L. Kimball (Salt Lake City: Bookcraft, 1982), p. 115.
8. Spencer W. Kimball, *Faith Precedes the Miracle* (Salt Lake City: Deseret Book, 1972), p. 208.
9. Howard W. Hunter, *Conference Report,* October 1988, p. 69.
10. Ezra Taft Benson, *Teachings of Ezra Taft Benson* (Salt Lake City: Bookcraft, 1988), p. 433.
11. *Journal of Discourses,* Vol. 8 (London: Latter-day Saints' Book Depot, 1854), p. 339.
12. Neal A. Maxwell, *All These Things Shall Give Thee Experience* (Salt Lake City: Deseret Book, 1980), p. 100.
13. Ibid., p. 92.
14. Blair Justice, *Who Gets Sick: Thinking and Health* (Houston, Tex.: Peak Press, 1987), p. 275.
15. Spencer W. Kimball, *BYU Speeches of the Year* (Provo, Utah: BYU Press, 1961).
16. Herbert Benson, *Your Maximum Mind* (New York: Times Books/Random House, Inc., 1987), p. 6.
17. Ibid., p. 46.
18. Russell M. Nelson, "Woman—Of Infinite Worth," *Ensign*, November 1989, p. 22.
19. Peter Barry Chowka, "Prayer Is Good Medicine," *Yoga Journal,* July/August 1996, pp. 63-64.
20. Dawson Church and Alan Serr, eds., *The Heart of the Healer* (New York: Aslan Publishing, 1987), p. 62.

21. Ibid., p. 63.
22. "Does Prayer Help Patients?" *MD,* December 1986, p. 35; and Blair Justice, *Who Gets Sick: Thinking and Health* (Houston, Tex.: Peak Press, 1987), p. 284.
23. *Newsday,* December 21, 1993.
24. Peter Barry Chowka, "Prayer Is Good Medicine," *Yoga Journal,* July/August 1996, p. 66.
25. Dawson Church and Alan Serr, eds., *The Heart of the Healer* (New York: Aslan Publishing, 1987), p. 63.
26. Blair Justice, *Who Gets Sick: Thinking and Health* (Houston, Tex.: Peak Press, 1987), pp. 284-85.
27. "Does Prayer Help Patients?" *MD,* December 1986, p. 35.
28. Ibid.
29. Ezra Taft Benson, *Teachings of Ezra Taft Benson* (Salt Lake City: Bookcraft, 1988), p. 422.
30. Ibid., p. 424.
31. Ibid.
32. Spencer W. Kimball, "Humility," *Improvement Era,* August 1963, p. 657.
33. Joseph F. Smith, *Gospel Doctrine,* 5th edition (Salt Lake City: Deseret Book, 1939), p. 219.
34. David O. McKay, *Secrets of a Happy Life,* comp. by Llewelyn R. McKay (Salt Lake City: Bookcraft, 1960), p. 114.
35. Ezra Taft Benson, *Teachings of Ezra Taft Benson* (Salt Lake City: Bookcraft, 1988), p. 432.
36. Neal A. Maxwell, *Deposition of a Disciple* (Salt Lake City: Deseret Book, 1976), p. 20.
37. Spencer W. Kimball, *BYU Speeches of the Year* (Provo, Utah: BYU Press, 1961).
38. Ezra Taft Benson, "To 'The Rising Generation,'" *The New Era,* June 1986, p. 8.
39. Neal A. Maxwell, *Deposition of a Disciple* (Salt Lake City: Deseret Book, 1976, p. 20.
40. Spencer W. Kimball, *BYU Speeches of the Year* (Provo, Utah: BYU Press, 1961).
41. H. Burke Peterson, *Conference Report,* October 1973, p. 13.

42. Boyd K. Packer, *Conference Report*, October 1979, p. 30.
43. Spencer W. Kimball, *The Teachings of Spencer W. Kimball*, comp. by Edward L. Kimball (Salt Lake City: Bookcraft, 1982), p. 77.
44. Neal A. Maxwell, *All These Things Shall Give Thee Experience* (Salt Lake City: Deseret Book, 1980), p. 93.
45. Ezra Taft Benson, "The Best Advice I Ever Had," *Reader's Digest,* November 1954, pp. 98-99.
46. Ezra Taft Benson, *Teachings of Ezra Taft Benson* (Salt Lake City: Bookcraft, 1988), pp. 424, 427-28, 434

A part of spiritual maturity occurs when we acknowledge that there is an unseen source of power and truth, "a profound realization that man does not stand alone."

— THE AUTHORS

I see a wonderful future in a very uncertain world. If we will cling to our values, if we will build on our inheritance, if we will walk in obedience before the Lord, if we will simply live the gospel we will be blessed in a magnificent and wonderful way. We will be looked upon as a peculiar people who have found the key to a peculiar happiness.

— President Gordon B. Hinckley

CONCLUSION

Ultimate Health: A Personal Responsibility

In study after study, members of The Church of Jesus Christ of Latter-day Saints have been found to live longer, healthier lives. Those who look for explanations point simply to the Word of Wisdom.

There is no question that the Word of Wisdom has tremendous impact on the health and longevity of Church members. A revelation received by Joseph Smith in 1833, it is so brief that it doesn't even fill both sides of a single page in the Doctrine and Covenants—but it is one of the most powerful prescriptions for health available today.

The U.S. Surgeon General has proclaimed that cigarette smoking is the number-one preventable cause of death in the United States. Tobacco use accounts for one of every six deaths, claiming more than 400,000 Americans every year. That's more than 1,000 people every day. What America's most skilled researchers have learned through decades of sophisticated testing was revealed to a young prophet more than 160 years ago: "tobacco is not for the body, neither for the belly, and is not good for man" (D&C 89:8).

It is not only their abstinence from tobacco that sets Latter-day Saints apart. Alcohol is America's number-one drug problem, with approximately 18 million suffering alcohol-related health problems. One in ten Americans is at least moderately addicted to alcohol, and an estimated nine of ten high school seniors report having used alcohol at least once. Alcohol is a factor in approximately half of all homicides, suicides, and motor vehicle fatalities. In fact, one in ten deaths in the United States each year is related to alcohol; heavy drinkers shave between fifteen and twenty years from their normal life expectancy. Fetal alcohol syndrome, caused when an unborn baby is exposed to alcohol in the womb, is the leading preventable cause of birth defects in this country.

What counsel did the Lord give to the Prophet Joseph that February afternoon in Kirtland, Ohio? "That inasmuch as any man drinketh wine or strong drink among you, behold it is not good, neither meet in the sight of your Father. . . . Strong drinks are not for the belly, but for the washing of your bodies" (D&C 89: 5, 7).

But probe more deeply into this simple, yet profound, revelation. After warning the Saints of the things that might harm them, the Lord shared his wisdom concerning ways to preserve health. In the last few years, the United States Department of Agriculture proposed a radical shift from the well-known four food groups. Instead, it gave us the "food pyramid," emphasizing the proportions that would lead to a healthy, balanced diet. At its base—the food that should make up the bulk of the diet, say the scientists—are the grains. The Lord's counsel in 1833? "All grain is ordained for the use of man and of beasts, *to be the staff of life*. . . . All grain is good for the food of man" (D&C 89:14, 16; emphasis added).

There's more. Science advises that we eat plenty of fresh fruits and vegetables. The Lord advises eating "every fruit in the season thereof" and "the fruit of the vine; that which yieldeth fruit, whether in the ground or above the ground" (D&C 89:11, 16). Researchers focus on saturated fats and warn against eating too much meat; the Lord warned that flesh "of beasts and of the fowls of the air . . . are to be used sparingly" (D&C 89:12). It is no wonder, then, that active Latter-day Saints have an edge on health and longevity.

But the Word of Wisdom, despite its powerful prescription, is only the beginning. Our loving Father in Heaven desires for his children the greatest possible joy—not only in mortality, but throughout all eternity. And so he, who knows all, has given a pattern for living guaranteed to provide not only joy, but ultimate wellness.

We know that social support is one of the most influential factors in good health and long life—and it is within the gospel pattern of living that we find some of the greatest examples of social support. It begins with marriage, and with the encouragement to marry by covenant in a temple of God. Elder Bruce C. Hafen aptly described the differences between what the Church prescribes and what the world imposes:

> When troubles come, the parties to a contractual marriage seek happiness by walking away. They marry to obtain benefits and will stay only as long as they're receiving what they bargained for. But when troubles come to a covenant marriage, the husband and wife work them through. They marry to give and to grow, bound by covenants to each other, to the community, and to God. Contract companions each give 50 percent; covenant companions each give 100 percent. Marriage is by nature a covenant, not just a private contract one may cancel at will.[1]

Closely related to marriage, of course, is the significance of the family. The family, which is one of the richest possible sources of social support, is important enough that it was the subject of the First Presidency's "Proclamation on the Family"—one of only a handful of public proclamations issued in the history of the Church. In describing the important role of the family, Elder Robert D. Hales said:

> While our individual salvation is based on our individual obedience, it is equally important that we understand that

> we are each an important and integral part of a family and the highest blessings can be received only within an eternal family. When families are functioning as designed by God, the relationships found therein are the most valued of mortality. The plan of the Father is that family love and companionship will continue into the eternities. . . . It is not enough just to save ourselves. It is equally important that parents, brothers, and sisters are saved in our families. If we return home to our Heavenly Father, we will be asked, "Where is the rest of the family?" That is why we teach that families are forever. The eternal nature of an individual becomes the eternal nature of the family.[2]

Opportunities for strong social support abound in the gospel plan, extending beyond marriage the family unit. We are taught to regard the ward as our family; we gather in meetings and at activities. We welcome into our homes visiting teachers and home teachers. We are encouraged, as President Thomas S. Monson stated, to emulate the Savior, who "lived not to be served, but to serve; not to receive, but to give; not to save His life, but to sacrifice it for others."[3]

Ours is a gospel that warns against anger, hostility, and contempt; it is a pattern for living that encourages forgiveness and love. We are taught to be optimistic, to look forward with hope and faith. All these are attitudes that contribute to deep spiritual peace as well as robust physical health and wellness. These—faith, hope, charity, prayer, and an unremitting desire to emulate the Savior, are, to a great degree, what brings health and long life to faithful Latter-day Saints.

As Jeffrey R. Holland so eloquently penned, it is the Savior and the gospel that can bring us the greatest healing of all:

> Jesus is the Christ, the Son of the living God. This is his true and living Church. He wishes us to come unto him, to follow him, to be comforted by him. Then he wishes us to give comfort to others. However halting our steps are towards him—though they shouldn't be halting at all—his

steps are never halting toward us. May we have enough faith to accept the goodness of God and the mercy of his Only Begotten Son. May we come unto him and his gospel and be healed. And may we do more to heal others in the process. When the storms of life make this difficult, may we still follow his bidding to "come," keeping our eye fixed on him forever and single to his glory. In doing so we too will walk triumphantly over the swelling waves of life's difficulties and remain unterrified amid any rising winds of despair.[4]

END NOTES

1. Bruce C. Hafen, "Covenant Marriage," Ensign, November 1996, p. 26.
2. Robert D. Hales, "The Eternal Family," *Ensign,* November 1996, p. 65.
3. Thomas S. Monson, "Home Teaching—A Divine Service," *Ensign,* November 1997, p. 48.
4. Jeffrey R. Holland, "Come Unto Me," *Ensign,* April 1998, p. 23.

Selected Bibliography

Barsky, Arthur J. *Worried Sick: Our Troubled Quest for Wellness.* Boston: Little, Brown, and Company, 1988.

Benson, Ezra Taft, *Teachings of Ezra Taft Benson.* Salt Lake City: Bookcraft, 1988.

Benson, Herbert. *Beyond the Relaxation Response.* New York: Times Books, 1984.

———. *The Mind/Body Effect.* New York: Simon and Schuster, 1979.

———, and Eileen M. Stuart. *The Wellness Book.* New York: Birch Lane Press, 1992.

Borysenko, Joan. *Fire in the Soul.* New York: Warner Books, 1993.

Brown, Hugh B. *The Abundant Life.* Salt Lake City: Bookcraft, 1965.

Burns, David D. *Feeling Good: The New Mood Therapy.* New York: New American Library, 1980.

Clark, James R. Clark, ed. *Messages of the First Presidency of The Church of Jesus Christ of Latter-day Saints.* Salt Lake City: Bookcraft, 1975.

Cohen, Sheldon and S. Leonard Syme, eds., *Social Support and Health.* London: Academic Press, Inc., 1985.

Cousins, Norman. *Head First: The Biology of Hope.* New York: E. P. Dutton, 1989.

Curran, Dolores. *Stress and the Healthy Family.* Minneapolis, Minn.: Winston Press, 1985.

———. *Traits of a Healthy Family* (Minneapolis, Minn.: Winston Press, 1983.

Dossey, Larry. *Healing Words.* San Francisco: Harper San Francisco, 1993.

Faust, James E. *Reach Up for the Light.* Salt Lake City: Deseret Book, 1990.

Faelten, Sharon, David Diamond, and the editors of *Prevention* magazine. *Take Control of Your Life: A Complete Guide to Stress Relief.* Emmaus, Penn.: Rodale Press, 1988.

Friedman, Howard S. *The Self-Healing Personality.* New York: Henry Holt and Company, 1991.

Hafen, Brent Q. and Kathryn J. Frandsen, *People Who Need People Are the Healthiest People: The Importance of Relationships.* Provo, Utah: Behavioral Health Associates, 1987.

———, Keith J. Karren, Kathryn J. Frandsen, N. Lee Smith. *Mind/Body Health: The Effects of Attitudes, Emotions, and Relationships*. Needham Heights, Mass.: Allyn and Bacon, 1996.

Hinckley, Gordon B. *Cornerstones of a Happy Home* (pamphlet), published by The Church of Jesus Christ of Latter-day Saints, Salt Lake City, 1984.

Justice, Blair. *Who Gets Sick: Thinking and Health.* Houston, Tex.: Peak Press, 1987.

Kimball, Spencer W. *Faith Precedes the Miracle.* Salt Lake City: Deseret Book, 1972.

———. *Marriage and Divorce*. Salt Lake City: Deseret Book, 1976.

———. *The Miracle of Forgiveness.* Salt Lake City: Bookcraft, 1969.

———. *Teachings of Spencer W. Kimball.* Comp. by Edward L. Kimball. Salt Lake City: Bookcraft, 1982.

Klein, Allen. *The Healing Power of Humor.* Los Angeles: Jeremy P. Tarcher, Inc., 1989.

Lee, Harold B. *Stand Ye In Holy Places: Selected Sermons and Writings of President Harold B. Lee.* Salt Lake City: Deseret Book, 1975.

Locke, Steven and Douglas Colligan. *The Healer Within.* New York: E.P. Dutton, 1986.

Ludlow, Daniel H., ed. *The Encyclopedia of Mormonism.* New York: Macmillan Publishers, 1992.

Lynch, James J. *The Broken Heart: The Medical Consequences of Loneliness*. New York: Basic Books, Inc., 1977.

Maxwell, Neal A. *All These Things Shall Give Thee Experience.* Salt Lake City: Deseret Book, 1980.

———. *Behold, I Say Unto You, I Cannot Say the Smallest Part Which I Feel.* Salt Lake City: Deseret Book, 1973.

———. *Deposition of a Disciple.* Salt Lake City: Deseret Book, 1976.

———. *For the Power Is in Them: Mormon Musings.* Salt Lake City: Deseret Book, 1970.
———. *Men and Women of Christ.* Salt Lake City: Bookcraft, 1991.
———. *A More Excellent Way: Essays on Leadership for Latter-day Saints.* Salt Lake City: Deseret Book, 1973.
———. *Notwithstanding My Weakness.* Salt Lake City: Deseret Book, 1981.
———. *That My Family Should Partake.* Salt Lake City: Deseret Book, 1974.
———. *Things As They Really Are.* Salt Lake City: Deseret Book, 1980.
———. *We Talk of Christ, We Rejoice in Christ.* Salt Lake City: Deseret Book, 1984.
———. *We Will Prove Them Herewith.* Salt Lake City: Deseret Book, 1982.
———. *Wherefore, Ye Must Press Forward.* Salt Lake City: Deseret Book, 1977.
McConkie, Bruce R. *Mormon Doctrine.* 2nd edition, revised. Salt Lake City, Utah: Bookcraft, 1966.
McKay, David O. *Gospel Ideals.* Comp. by G. Homer Durham. Salt Lake City: The Improvement Era, 1953.
Metcalf, C.W. and Roma Felible. *Lighten Up: Survival Skills for People Under Pressure* Reading, Mass.: Addison-Wesley Publishing Company, Inc.
Ornstein, Robert and David Sobel. *Healthy Pleasures.* Reading, Mass.: Addison-Wesley Publishing Company, Inc., 1989.
———. and Charles Swencionis, eds. *The Healing Brain: A Scientific Reader.* New York: The Guilford Press, 1990.
Padus, Emrika. *The Complete Guide to Your Emotions and Your Health.* Emmaus, Penn.: Rodale Press, 1986.
Pearsall, Paul. *Super Joy: Learning to Celebrate Everyday Life.* New York: Doubleday, 1988.
Pelletier, Kenneth. *Sound Mind, Sound Body: A New Model for Lifelong Health.* New York: Simon and Schuster, 1994.
Pilisuk, Marc and Susan Hillier Parks. *The Healing Web.* Hanover, N.H.: The University Press of New England, 1986.

Positive Living and Health: The Complete Guide to Brain/Body Healing and Mental Empowerment. Ed. by *Prevention* Magazine and the Center for Positive Living. Emmaus, Penn.: Rodale Press, 1990.

Powell, Barbara. *Alone, Alive, and Well.* Emmaus, Penn.: Rodale Press, 1985.

Rice, Phillip L. *Stress and Health: Principles and Practice for Coping and Wellness.* Monterey, Calif.: Brooks/Cole Publishing Company, 1987.

Sagan, Leonard A. *The Health of Nations.* New York: Basic Books, Inc., 1987.

Seligman, Martin E.P., *Learned Optimism.* New York: Alfred A. Knopf, 1991.

Siegel, Bernie S. *Love, Medicine, and Miracles.* New York: Harper and Row, 1986.

———. *Peace, Love, and Healing.* New York: Harper and Row, 1989.

Silverstone, T. and C. Thompson, eds. *Seasonal Affective Disorder.* London: Clinical Neuroscience Publishers, 1989.

Smith, George Albert. *Sharing the Gospel with Others.* Salt Lake City: Deseret Book.

Smith, Joseph Fielding. *Doctrines of Salvation: Sermons and Writings of Joseph Fielding Smith.* Ed. by Bruce R. McConkie. Salt Lake City: Bookcraft, 1955.

———, ed. *Teachings of the Prophet Joseph Smith.* Salt Lake City: Deseret Book, 1938.

Stroebe, Wolfgang and Margaret S. Stroebe, *Bereavement and Health.* Cambridge, Mass.: Cambridge University Press, 1987.

Stuy, Brian H., ed., *Collected Discourses.* Burbank, Calif., and Woodland Hills, Utah: BHS Publishing Company, 1987.

Talmage, James E. *Jesus the Christ.* 15th edition, revised. Salt Lake City: The Church of Jesus Christ of Latter-day Saints, 1977.

Widtsoe, John A., comp. *Discourses of Brigham Young.* Salt Lake City: Deseret Book, 1978.

INDEX

A

B

D

E

F

G

H

N

O

S

U

V

W

Y

Z